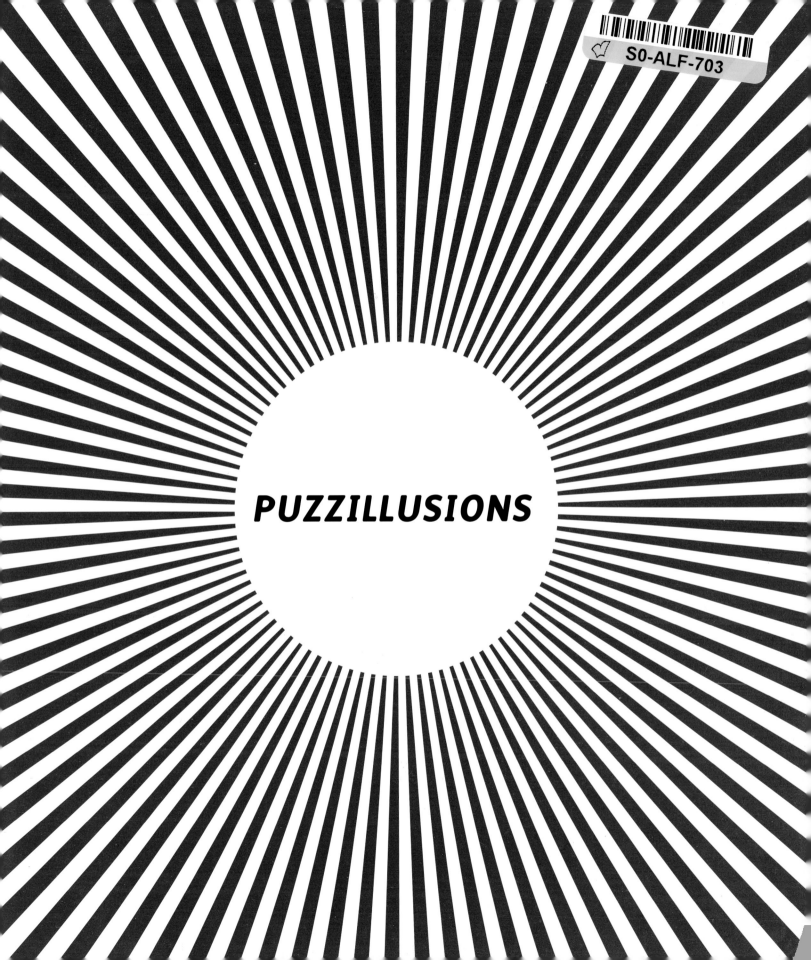

PUZZILLUSIONS

Authors' dedication:
To Mireille Schumacher, our friend and suggester,
who is above all a nuclear reaction of creativity and passion for mathematics and its popularization.

This 2007 edition published by Barnes & Noble, Inc.,
by arrangement with Carlton Books Limited
20 Mortimer Street, London W1T 3JW

ISBN-13: 978-0-7607-9346-6
ISBN-10: 0-7607-9346-8

1 3 5 7 9 10 8 6 4 2

Printed in Dubai

FURTHER READING:
Mathematics, Magic and Mystery by Martin Gardner, Dover Publications.
Practical Mental Magic by Theodore Annemann, Dover Publications.
MateMagica by Gianni A. Sarcone, La Meridiana.
Dissections: Plane and Fancy by Greg N. Frederickson, Cambridge University Press.
Big Book of Optical Illusions by Gianni Sarcone and Marie-Jo Waeber, Barron's Educational.

CREDITS:
Page 83: The image is based on a computer drawing of Craig S. Kaplan.

PUZZILLUSIONS

More than 125 Optical Illusions and
Puzzles Combined!

Gianni A. Sarcone
& Marie-Jo Waeber,
www.archimedes-lab.org

CARLTON

Contents

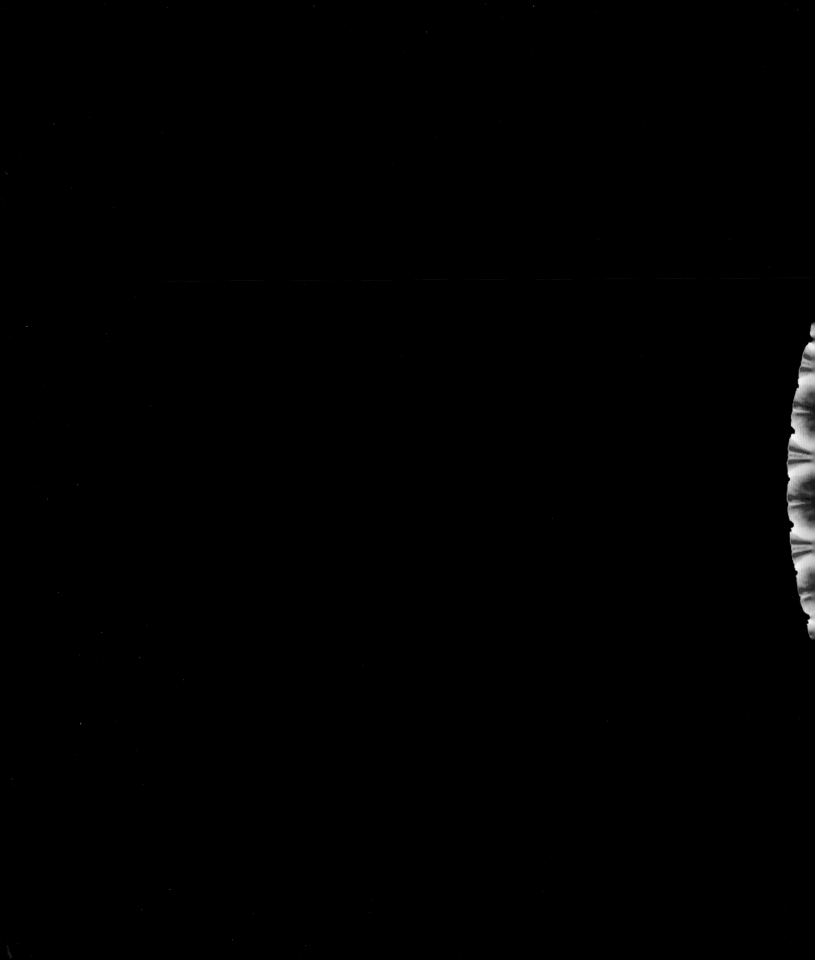

Foreword

The writer Anatole France once said, "Awaken people's curiosity. It is enough to open minds; do not overload them … put there just a spark!" From this simple statement I found the idea for my career.

As an author, columnist and researcher in the field of teaching methodology and visual thinking, I have always tried to combine psychology, cognitive science and mathematics to test people's ingenuity. I know by experience people love doing simple puzzles that involve counterintuitive or paradoxical surprises. Inventing or adapting such puzzles has been my job for 20 years. I am still not tired of the pleasure I experience when a reader/player is amazed by the simplicity, the ingenuity or the oddity of a solution to a puzzle I propose.

What interests me is to communicate ideas about the development and stimulation of thinking. To study the common misdirections that can mislead our cognitive processes. To detect the mental blocks which prevent us from finding a solution to a problem. To examine the links between imagination, creativity and logical reasoning. I have found that optical illusions, puzzles and brainteasers combine all those fields of interest amazingly well!

Puzzles are not closed problems. They can always be modified or improved to generate a myriad of variants. What is more, they do not require batteries because our own brain cells power them. To solve the perplexing and tricky puzzles assembled in this book, the reader will need a very high IQ. This is not the usual Intelligence Quotient, but *Inveniens Quaerendo* ("Trial and Error", your capacity for learning by attempting). Intelligence is not what you feel or what you know, but a problem solving skill. Everyone can acquire or develop problem-solving skills simply by training themselves at their own pace and relying on their existing knowledge. In the world of the mind, the race is not always to the swift, but to those who keep running. Even if the beginning may be discouraging, things will get better and better just by planning regular puzzle training sessions.

The beginner and seasoned puzzle fan, as well as teachers and trainers, will discover in this book a collection of classic and original visual puzzles, paradoxes and curiosities to tease their grey matter and rattle their ego. Clear but not so easy, these puzzles may even be used as resource material for educational or aptitude tests. Of course, they are intended for the general public, not for impatient and sober-minded mathematicians! We have endeavored to present intuitive puzzles with a medium level of difficulty, but high in terms of instructiveness and fun. These are the fruits of our work harvested during our workshops and exhibition tours. We offer them to you with great pleasure.

We have taken the greatest care in reading the proofs and trust that in this book there is at least just one important error (can you find it?) If you should find any extra error, we can only plead, in the words of C. S. Lewis, "Two heads are better than one, not because either is infallible, but because they are unlikely to go wrong in the same direction."

We have to express our special thanks to the team at Carlton Books who allow us to design, realize and share our passion with readers for the amusing exploration of the infinite mysteries of the human mind.

To conclude, Dear Reader, remember intelligence begins with a piece of paper, a pencil and a problem to solve. The ancient Greeks used to say Αρχη 'ημισυ παντος (Archê hêmisu pantos – starting on a job is half the job done). Now it is time to lean your brain forward and start thinking!

Gianni A. Sarcone
Game designer and co-founder of Archimedes-lab.org

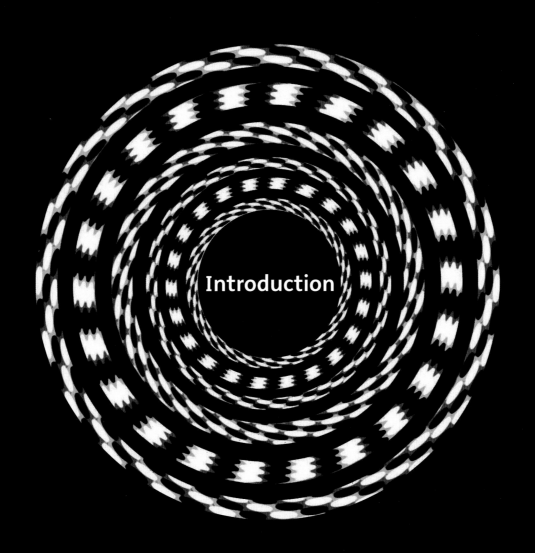

Introduction

Know yourself!

One day, walking and talking with his disciples, Plato affirmed: "You can discover more about a person in an hour of play than in a year of conversation." That is remarkably true for puzzles.

The fact we are all individuals is one of the main characteristic of the human nature. Each person is different in regard to the way he or she learns or solves a problem. Some of us are visual, some are more auditory and others are more sensitive and receptive to spatial tactile stimuli. That is why, when solving puzzles, some will proceed by deductive reasoning (from general to particular), some by inductive reasoning (from particular to general) and others by analogy (linking a problem to a real-life experience). There is more than one way to solve a problem. In fact, puzzles may help us understand our true nature. The way we solve them can unconsciously show:

• Who we are
• What we value
• How we regard others and our environment

For this reason we have tried to fill this puzzle anthology with the largest possible variety of visual illusions and puzzles to fit the propensity of any puzzle-solver. We wish to help you to find your true nature and use it to solve as many of the puzzles as possible collected in this book.

So, in the following pages you will find three major categories of puzzles:

– Perceptive puzzles. A little bit of insight and an inquisitive mind should be all the reader needs to solve them. These puzzles are aimed at improving the mental flexibility of the reader.

– Visual illusions. These are interactive visual thinking tests that help the reader to enhance his or her power of observation and critical thinking skills.

– Tactile manipulatives. Patterns or experiences the reader may reproduce or perform in order to build a tridimensional puzzle. This allows the reader to place and solve in a concrete context some abstract problems, helping to develop basic math concepts. Whilst making math puzzles tangible in this virtual era may seem anachronistic, a screen will never take the place of hands-on experience.

As you can see, some puzzles can be solved using only logical reasoning or the power of observation, while others need a pencil. A few others are more practical and need some sheets of paper, scissors and other everyday objects. When necessary, the reader can reproduce some patterns using a scanner or a photocopier.

> "A world without problems is an illusion; so is a world without solutions." Gianni A. Sarcone

Solving puzzles

After having boned up on a mathematical theorem, a student who was attending geometry courses under the tuition of the famous mathematician Euclid asked the teacher: "Sir, what will I earn by learning all these things?" On hearing this Euclid called his assistant and told him sarcastically to 'give the boy three coins, as he wants to make money from what he learns.'

The search for knowledge – without looking for profit or immediate returns – is often taken as a defining characteristic of intelligence. It has been said the extraordinary curiosity of humans makes us a unique species. What motivates man in his curiosity? At the dawn of mankind, curiosity was a synonym for life and survival. This might no longer be the case, but mankind seems even more inquisitive now than he was in the past. Today newspapers, radio, television, Internet are all unending sources of information. This information floods into our homes day and night to satisfy our hunger to know things, to learn and to be informed. This happens to such an extent the supply of information becomes unmanageable and so the gathering of knowledge requires complex filtering to determine what are good and useful data.

Some scientists regard curiosity as what motivates all our exploratory behavior, including playing. Curiosity can also be considered a measurement of the mental tonus and an antidote against boredom. Everything can be a source of knowledge. Even facts or things that seem worthless, inefficient, useless, absurd, odd, paradoxical or false may be instructive. It is worth remembering that Europeans discovered America because Columbus made a navigational error!

Puzzles capture people's attention because curiosity is a natural propensity. Puzzles are also intriguing, challenging and fun as well. Solving puzzles is one of the highest expressions of curiosity.

Treat with caution someone who says, "I have never ever solved a puzzle in my life!" It is difficult to know exactly what he or she means, as every intelligent individual is solving puzzles in some form every day. The only place where you will find people that really do not solve problems is the graveyard! If there were no puzzles to solve, there would be no questions to ask. If there were no questions to be asked, what a world it would be! A world without problems is an illusion; so is a world without solutions…

When it comes to the resolution of puzzles or other logic problems, the writers of this book have a simple philosophy; try and try again, always try and never give up. Do not worry about mistakes, as they are useful steps for climbing towards knowledge. If you do not know the background of a particular problem (formula, theory etc.) ask someone who knows! Asking and searching for knowledge is an important part of learning.

Just a word about mathematics… Every man, woman or child who works out the answer to the simplest puzzle is working, perhaps unconsciously, along mathematical lines. Even those puzzles we have no way of attacking except by haphazard attempts can be brought under a method known to some as glorified trial-and-error – a mathematical system of shortening our labors by avoiding or eliminating what our reason tells us is useless. Sometimes it is not easy to say where the empirical begins and where it ends.

In writing puzzle books, our main vision – possibly somewhat utopian – is to promote the puzzle as an educational aid useful for socialization and communication. Games and puzzles can increase players' self-confidence in their ability to apply knowledge to new situations. In the same way, players can learn the skills of collaborating, managing emotions and resolving conflicts in groups. We have always encouraged integrated approaches to thinking and learning. Integrated approaches enable adults and children to investigate a specific subject using many forms of knowledge and expression. This involves combining critical thinking, practical skills and topics from other subjects, as well as connecting the puzzle to the subjects' own lives and environment.

"Chance favors the prepared mind." Louis Pasteur

Are all puzzles logical or mathematical?

Some puzzles can be solved using logical thinking while others such as verbal puzzles can be figured out only by using correlative thinking. Rational or logical thinking stresses the explanatory power of physical causation (i.e. what causes what). In contrast, correlative thinking involves the association of image or concept-clusters related by meaningful disposition rather than physical causation.

Correlative thinking is important in our everyday life. The faculty of making fortunate discoveries by accident is not due only by chance, but is always combined with correlative thinking or in other words, the ability to see things differently. Some of the most important scientific discoveries – X-rays, penicillin, insulin, aspirin, safety glass, nylon, Teflon®, Velcro® and the transistor – may appear to be simply a matter of chance, but behind the chance lay in wait a prepared mind!

It is hard to understand why a lot of people fear or have a kind of irrational inferiority complex about logical thinking. Some ask if logic means being clever or if logic is more important than imagination... Logic is just a tool, one of the many implements of the mind (try to imagine our mind as a Swiss Army knife with a tool fit for each occasion). No, logic is not more important than imagination, but we can be creative and use the logic to increase our creativity. There should be no conflict between logic, imagination and intuition because they all complement each other.

What is the main difference between logic and ingenuity? You cannot learn ingenuity and it is present at variable degrees in nearly everyone of us. However, you can learn logic, since logic, unlike common sense, is not a natural cognitive process. It is important to know that logic and common sense often collide – in this book you will find some puzzles that depict this peculiarity.

Is logic appropriate for all ages? There is probably no correct answer to that question, but in each human life there is a time for logical reasoning and a time for playing and discovering. For young children it is natural that imagination is the rule, reasoning is the exception.

Is logic useful? In the world of mathematics and social sciences, logic investigates and classifies the structure of statements and arguments. The extent and importance of logic are therefore massive. It ranges from core topics such as the study of fallacies and paradoxes to specialized analyses of reasoning such as probability and arguments involving causality.

However, there is quite a bit of conflict between the way certain words are used in everyday language and how the same words are used in logic. Logic uses precisely defined words, whilst our normal native tongues are much more vague and ambiguous. Due to its ambiguity, many meaning traps are hidden in our everyday language and the use of logic can help us to detect them. When someone innocently asks you, "Have you stopped drinking too much lately?" or "Are you prepared to renounce negative thinking?" do not answer too quickly… Whether you answer yes or no, you admit your abuse of alcohol or your pessimism. What if a man says, "Sorry; I always lie"? If he always lies, then his statement itself must be a lie, which means that he is telling the truth… But if he is telling the truth, then he always lies which is a contradiction!

Here is another example of logic trap found in a newspaper. Most historians have few doubts of the Genoese origins of Christopher Columbus because Columbus himself maintained his Genoese ethnicity throughout his life. However, a laboratory for genetic identification at the University of Granada made a series of investigations on behalf of Catalonia at the beginning of the year 2006. They aimed at scientifically determining his provenance, as Catalonia also claims it was the birthplace of Columbus. The newspaper reported: "The mystery remains unsolved after DNA studies have so far been unable to lay to rest claims that Columbus was not Italian." We all generally encounter problems with double negation and therefore may translate the sentence into a simple message such as "there are serious doubts about his Italian origins" – despite the fact the sentence means the exact opposite! (If you find the Columbus example easy to unravel, try guessing if someone who argues "I do not dislike the opponents of the anti-vegetarians" is a vegetarian friend or foe?)

Here is a final curiosity… As you may have noticed, affirmation and negation are the lifeblood of logic. However, the way that yes or no are used in language may be quite different from country to country. In Japan, for instance, when you are asked whether you are hungry or not, to confirm, you should say: "No, I am hungry." When a negative form of interrogation is used, Japanese people deny the negation to reply affirmatively!

For those who wish to go deeper in their understanding of logic, the writers recommend *Logic for Beginners Through Games, Jokes and Puzzle*s by Irving Adler.

A brief history of puzzles

It might seem curious to some that most currently used words employed in the world of puzzling find their origins in Old French. The word puzzle itself comes from *pusle* – meaning to bewilder or confound. *Pusle* is a frequentative of the obsolete verb *pose* (from Medieval French *aposer*) in the sense of perplex. The meaning of the word puzzle as game, toy or problem contrived to test one's ingenuity is relatively recent, dating to the mid-19th century.

What are the origin of puzzles and mathematical games? Their origin is concealed in the innermost depths of our brain. In fact, sometimes man appears to let himself go into an abstracted 'diversion' that involves assembling or arranging pieces, counters or any small familiar object into patterns. This compulsive behavior seems to be evidence of a natural and irrepressible geometrical sense. It may be linked to the behavior that instinctively drives some birds to collect and group shells, glittering or colored objects. Assembling a puzzle may be not only an intellectual activity, but also a primitive geometric urge.

Puzzles, riddles and mathematical recreations may actually share a common origin. The 'Rhind Papyrus' (dated circa 1650 BCE) showed that early Egyptian mathematics was largely based on puzzle-type problems. For instance, the papyrus contained the following puzzle: "Seven houses contain seven cats. Each cat kills seven mice. Each mouse had eaten seven ears of grain. Each ear of grain would have produced seven hekats of wheat. What is the total of all of these?"

Most modern popular puzzles are just old disguised puzzles. We could credit 70% of popular puzzles to the following authors (named in chronological order): Alcuin of York, Leonardo Pisano (Fibonacci), Nicolas Chuquet, Luca Pacioli, Girolamo Cardano, Nicolò Tartaglia, Claude Gaspar Bachet de Mériziac, Claude Mydorge, Jacques Ozanam, William Hooper, Leonhard Euler, Edouard Lucas, Charles Lutwidge Dodgson (Lewis Carroll), Henry Dudeney. Let us also not forget Martin Gardner, one of the greatest puzzle compilers and inventors of the 20th century.

It is significant that most puzzle authors are also mathematicians or related to the world of numbers as philosophers, teachers or accountants. This may provide the evidence that mathematicians can sometimes, in their own way, be amusing.

Survival Tips to Solve Challenging Puzzles

As already discussed, usually there are often several different ways to solve a puzzle. However, in some cases there is only one. It is rare that a problem has no solution, though if that is the case, it can be argued that the solution consists of finding that the problem has no solution!

Sarcone & Waeber's rules for puzzle solving

- Nothing is as difficult as it looks.

- Nothing is as easy as it looks.

- Misdirection is very common in puzzles. Expert puzzle authors always try to lead people's minds along false trails.

- Recognize clearly what you have to search for, what data are useful and what are the relationships between the searched result and the data.

- Elements that appear to have no relevance may be fundamental and vice versa.

- Omissions (what is not written or said) are sometimes as important as the instructions given.

- Beware of subconscious restrictions and mental blocks; try to depart from the norms and stereotypes and look beyond the boundaries of a problem.

- Break a complex puzzle into smaller, manageable parts.

- Ensure that the puzzle has been considered from all points of view.

- With logic, correlated elements or events are not necessarily related. Some could just be coincidence.

- Likewise, correlated events may have a common cause. In fact, some correlations may not be relations between cause and effect but represent two effects of some other cause.

- Either of two correlated events may cause the other.

- Sometimes, to understand a problem, you'll need to use collective intelligence. Do not hesitate to ask someone else to help you.

- Use your intuition and deliberately try to find other ways to solve a puzzle.

- Sometimes the solution is what causes the problem. Avoid finding solutions to nonexistent problems, and never fix what is not broken.

- Enjoy making mistakes. Regard them as important and fruitful stages on the road to success.

- Be persistent; the joy of achievement is greater when it is preceded by a tough creative effort!

- Puzzles always have one, several or no solutions.

Have fun, and good luck!

PUZZILLUSIONS

THE MAGIC WARDROBE
Which green line seems larger: line AB or line CD?

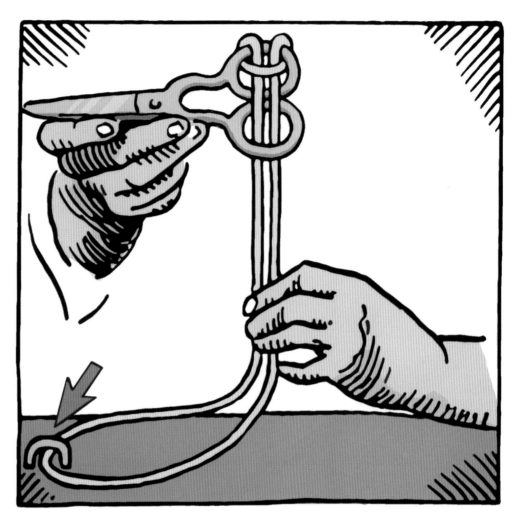

THE GREAT ESCAPE
Is it possible to free the scissors from the ring of rope without cutting it?
As you can see, a hooked nail holds the string to a desk.

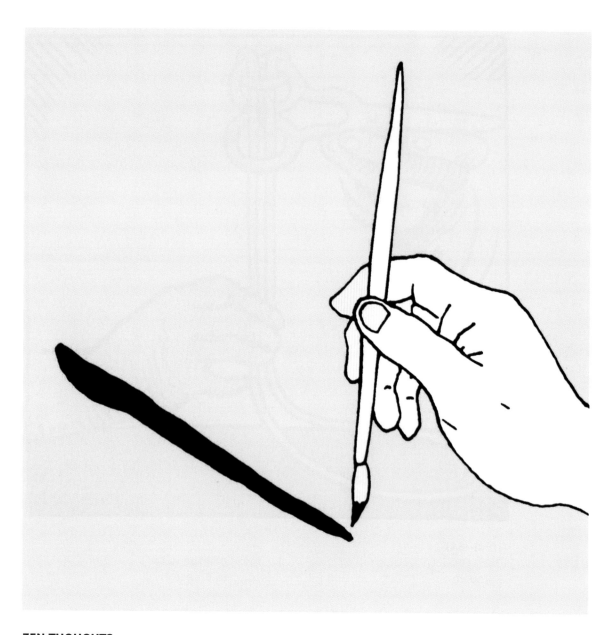

ZEN THOUGHTS
Is it possible to make the painted line shorter without touching any part of it?

BOX CLEVER
Sure, it's easy to draw two squares using all eight dots,
but can you delimit just one perfect square (the ring)
by connecting all the dots?

PERFECT TOP HAT
How tall is the top hat of this gentleman in proportion to the maximum width AB? At first glance it seems evident that AB is less than CD. Is this correct?

SWISS CROSS
Copy and cut out the four shapes above. Then assemble them to form a cross. It's not as obvious as it seems!

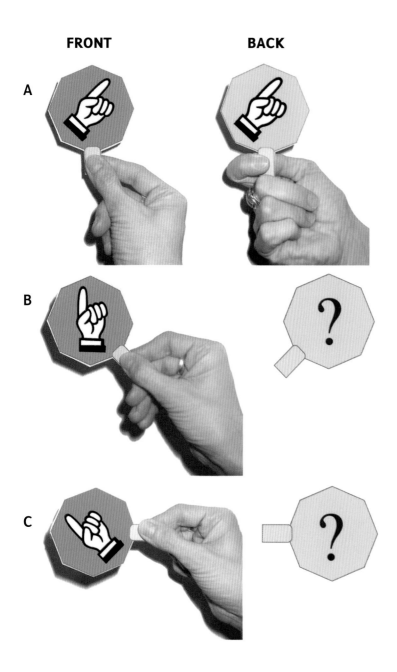

FRONT   **BACK**

A

B

C

GIVING DIRECTIONS
A pointed finger is printed on both sides of an octagonal
racket. Try to guess which direction the finger points to in B
and C.

TIED UP
Can you guess which line of colored squares is most like the decorative pattern in the middle of the tie? Is it A, B or C?

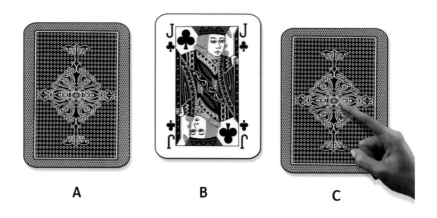

A   B   C

MAGIC PROBABILITIES

There are on the table three playing cards, face-down. You have to guess which one is a King of Spades. You point to card C. However, when you do that, the host of the game turns over card B and reveals it is not the King of Spades. Now, if you change your mind and select card A instead of C, what are your winning probabilities?

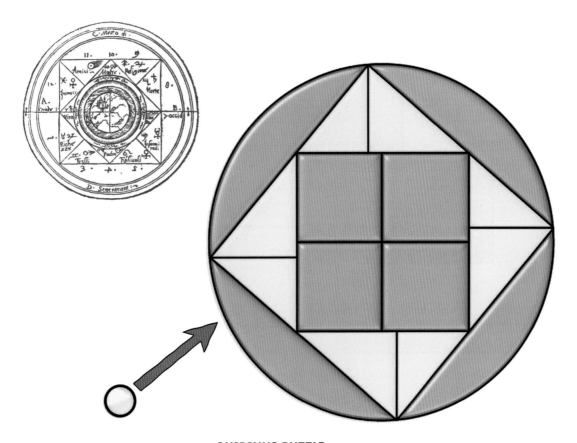

QUIRINUS PUZZLE
Astrology tables inspired this magical puzzle. Is it possible
to fit the small disk into the large one without apparently
changing its dimensions and with no missing pieces or
overlapping? You can reproduce and cut out the puzzle and
the small disk along the cutting lines and try to solve it
with your friends.

SHAPESHIFTER

How many regular shapes is it possible to form using the two triangles and the square shown in the illustration?
The only rule here is that the sides of the triangles and the square have to join together perfectly.

CONVERGING OR DIVERGING?
Do the radial lines really meet together at the center of the
disk? Are you sure?

ARCHIMEDES LOGO

Glue a copy of the puzzle above on to thin cardboard and cut along the lines to obtain 12 rectangular cards. The aim of the game is to assemble the square again making 12 Archimedes logos appear.

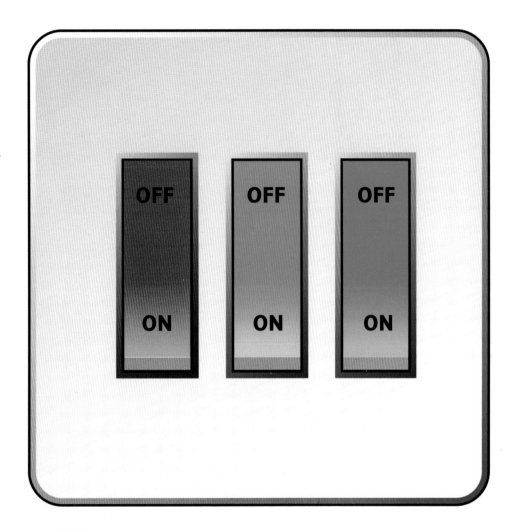

SWITCHED ON

On a wall are three standard on/off switches. Only one controls a lightbulb inside a lightproof, well-insulated closet. The other two switches do nothing. You can only open the closet door once and cannot touch any switches once the door is open. Within these constraints, can you determine with certainty which switch controls the light bulb?

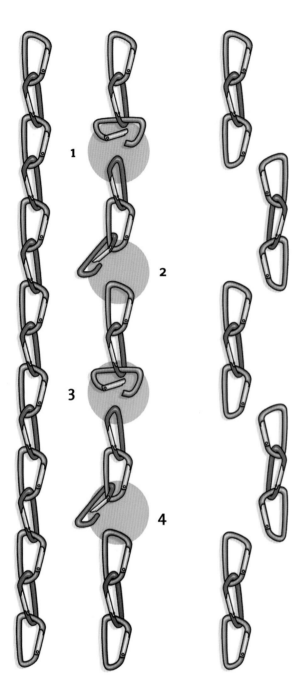

CHAINED

A chain of 15 linked snap-hooks can be separated into five smaller parts by opening just four single snap-hooks. Is it possible to link together the five chain portions to form the initial chain again by opening only three single snap-hooks?

FILL IN
Can you complete the drawing? Try to make a coherent image using your sense of humor.

MEMORY TEST

Spend approximately 10 seconds looking at the drawing on this page and try to remember it. Then take a paper sheet and reproduce the pattern.

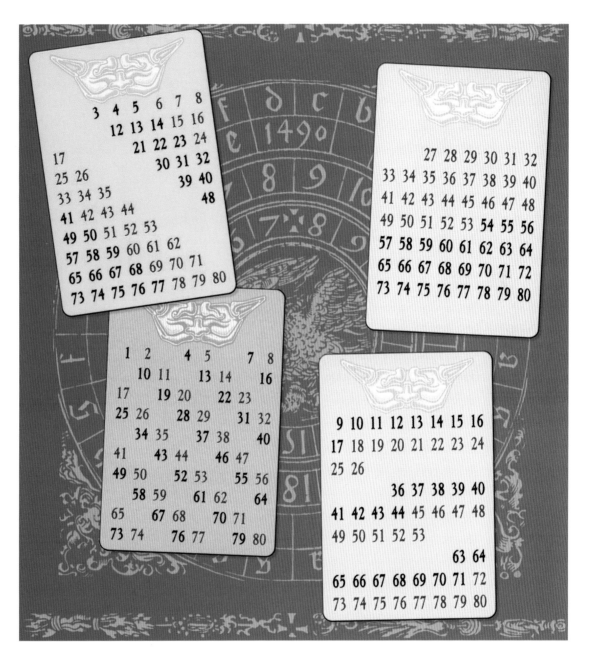

MATHEMATICAL MIND-READING

Here is an interesting self-working mind-reading trick. Four color cards feature red and black sets of numbers. Ask someone to pick a number from 1 to 80. Then show him/her each card, one at a time, and ask "Is your number on this card? If yes, is it red or black?" After you have shown all four cards, you should guess the thought number. Can you work out how this trick works?

A

B

ROUND-TRIP

Imagine you leave for your holidays with your caravan and go to Wonga (B), the paradise of the puzzlers. The day is clear, you are happy and drive 80 miles/hour on the motorway. Arriving at Wonga, you realize you have forgotten your dog and immediately return home (A) to collect it, driving at 120 miles/hour back on the motorway. Can you say now what was the average speed during your trip from A to B and return to A?

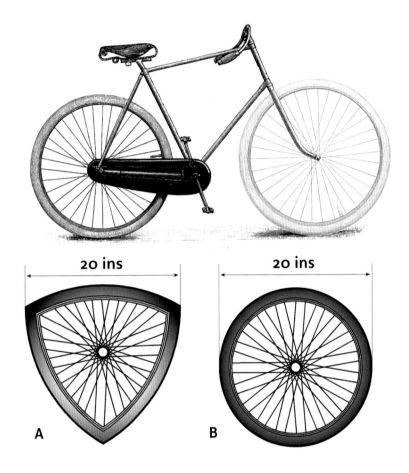

20 ins   **20 ins**

A   B

ROUND AND ROUND

Observe the wheel A. Each side of the triangular wheel is regular and is an arc centered on the opposite vertex. Can we cover with wheel A the same distance by pedalling the same number of turns as wheel A? Try to imagine a mechanical system which permits wheel A to be fitted to the bike in such a way as to allow for a comfortable ride without bouncing up and down!

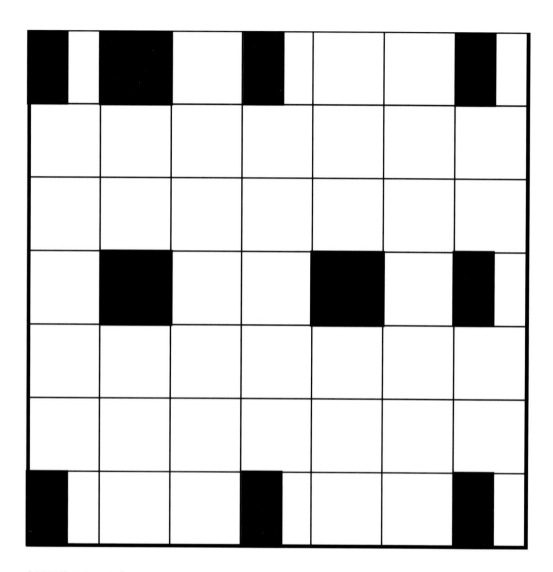

CAN YOU SEE IT?
A word is hidden in this crossword grid, but can you find it?

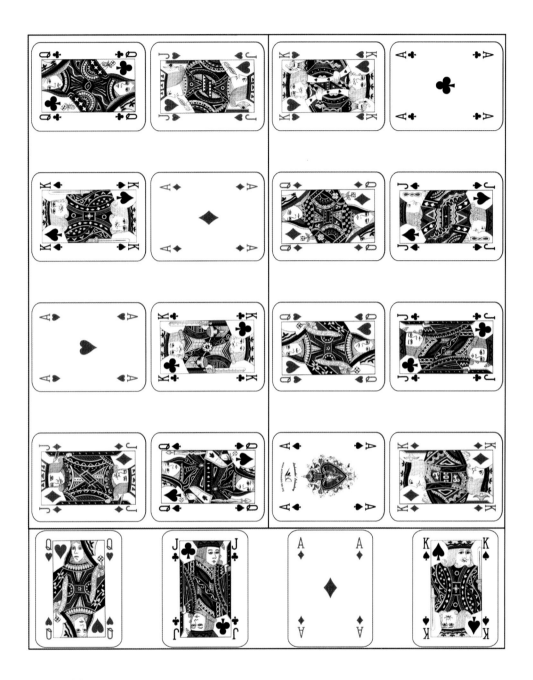

ROYAL COURT

Reproduce the set of playing cards and cut it into three pieces along the cutting lines. Then arrange the three rectangular pieces in order to obtain a square of four by four playing cards so that each row and each column contains an Ace, a King, a Queen and a Jack of different suits. Overlapping is allowed.

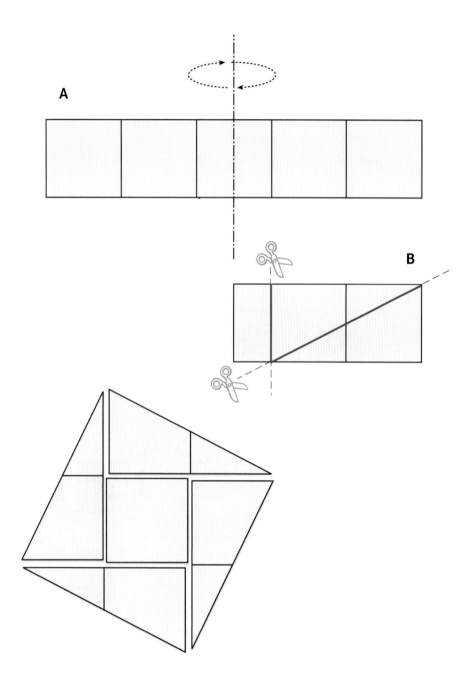

SQUARED
By folding (A) and cutting twice (B) the paper strip shown in the illustration, you can get five pieces with which you can form a square. Now, can you fold and cut twice the same strip and get only four pieces to form a perfect square again?

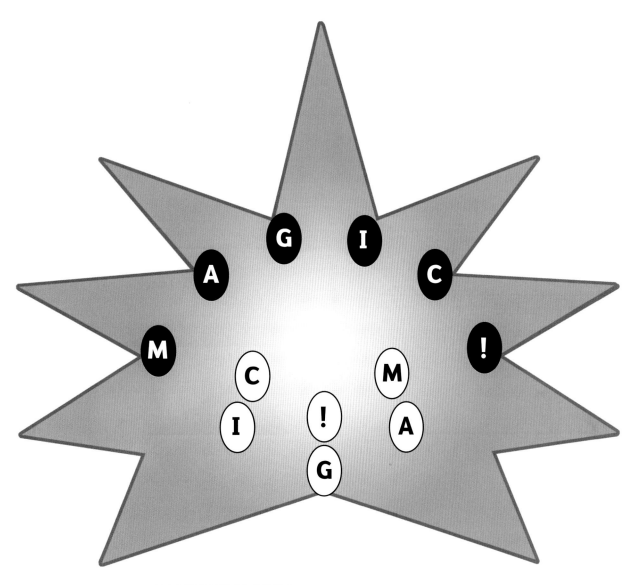

MAGIC PATH PROBLEM
Can you take a pencil and draw lines to join each white
letter to its black counterpart (M to M, A to A, etc.),
without any line crossing another line.

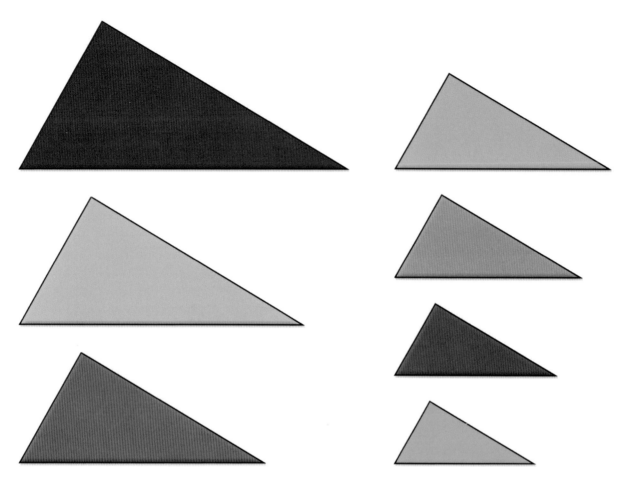

TRIANGLES TO SQUARE
Copy the seven color triangles and fit them together to form a square (no overlapping). Is it possible to make a rectangle with the same pieces?

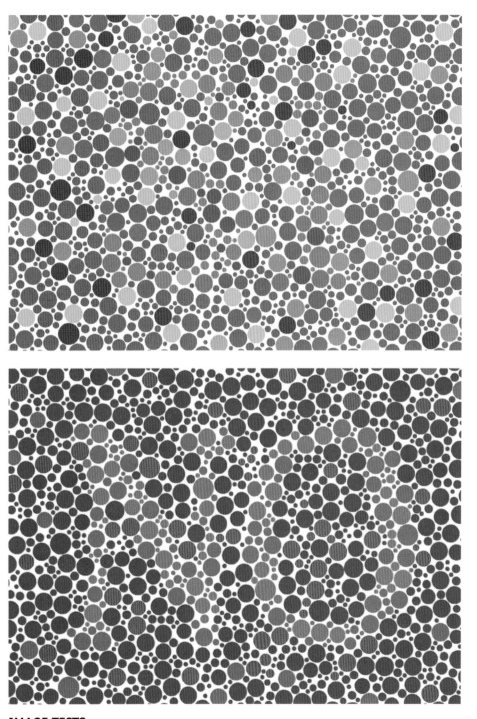

IMAGE TESTS
Observe both images. What capital letters do you see revealed in the patterns of dots?

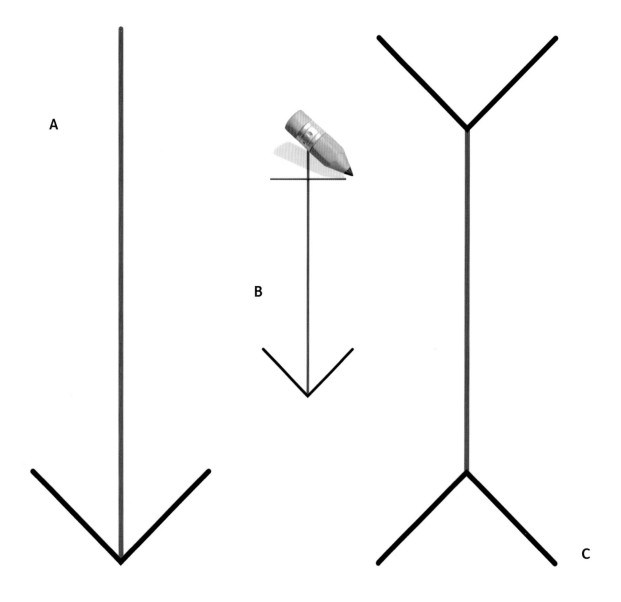

HOW LONG?
Take a pencil and draw a short stroke on the vertical red line A (as illustrated in fig. B) to mark, at a rough guess, the boundary of its height so that it matches the height of the red line C. Then measure both lines with a ruler. We bet your line is longer!

CHINOISERIES
Which one of the three men depicted in the illustration
is the tallest?

THE RIGHT ANGLE
One of the angles of the tubular cross is exactly 90 degrees. Help the Sun King's architect, Jean Vidocq, to find it.

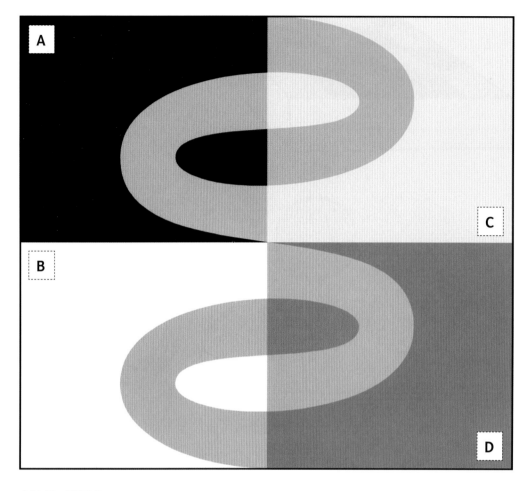

COLOR CURVE
Are the curvilinear patterns in the rectangles A, B and C, D of the same shade?

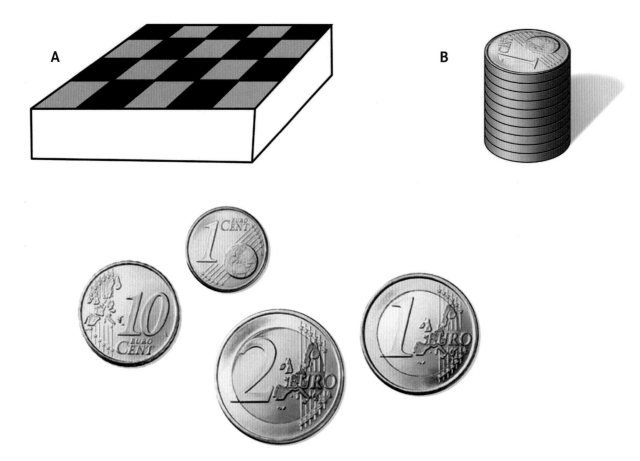

CASH CONUNDRUM
Which of the four coins exactly covers the height of the gray checkerboard A? Which coin has a diameter that matches exactly the height of the stack of coins B?

A   B   C   D

DOME DILEMMA
Which color is the golden onion-shaped
dome of St Petersburg's church: A, B, C or D?

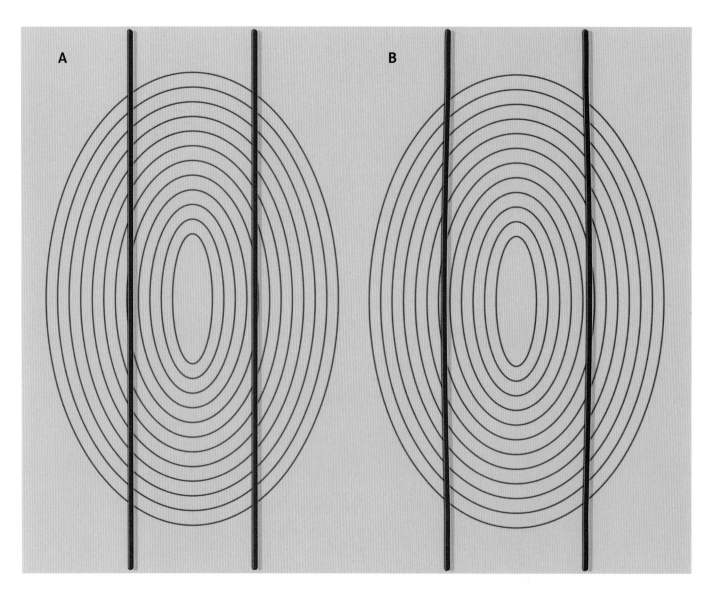

DISTORTED LINES
Which pair of red lines are perfectly straight and parallel, A or B?

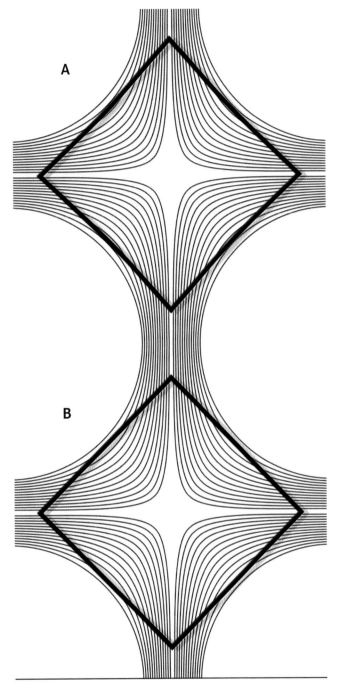

THE MORE SQUARED SQUARE
Which of these squares is really square, A or B?

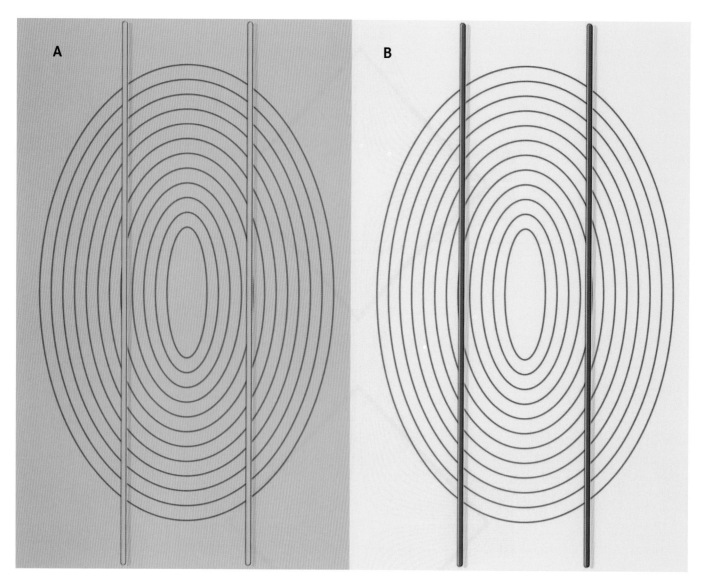

LINE UP
Which pair of lines are perfectly straight and parallel, A or B?

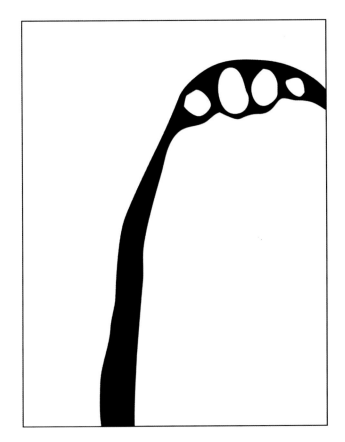 

MYSTERIOUS DRAWINGS
What do both drawings represent?

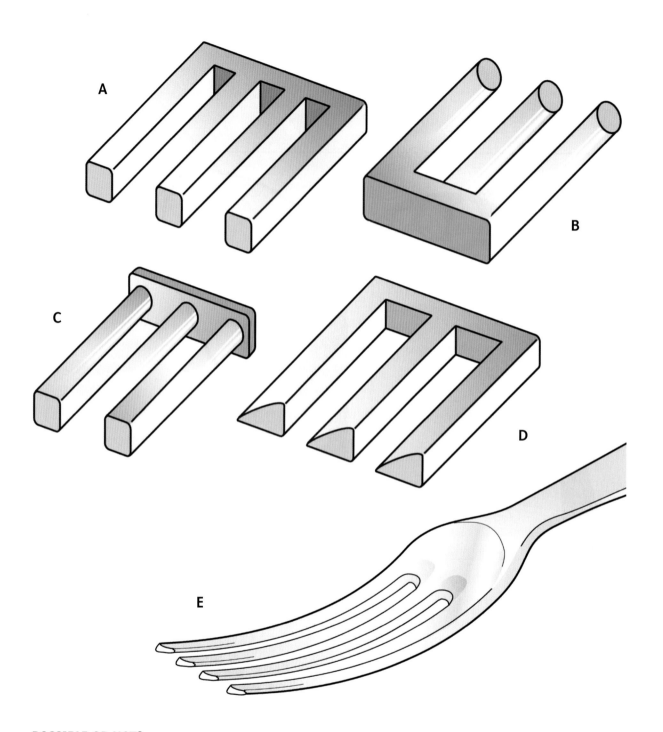

POSSIBLE OR NOT?
Which one of these objects really exists?

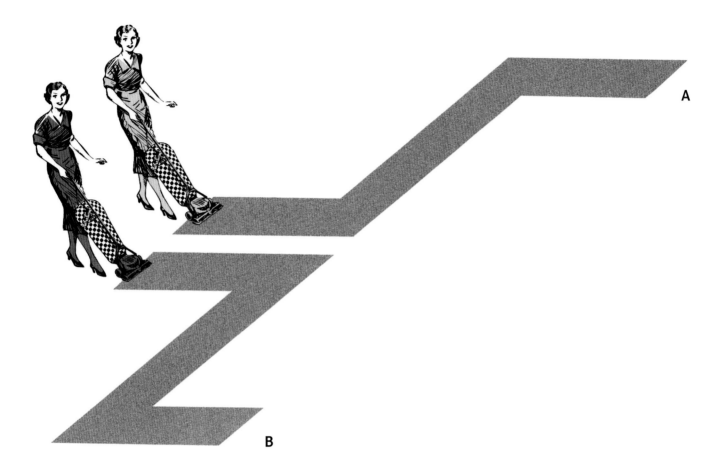

CARPETS

At the Palace Hotel, two cleaners have to vacuum the carpets in the corridors on the first floor. In your opinion, who has less work to do: the one with carpet A or the one with carpet B?

TANGRAMAGIC

This is an intriguing vanish puzzle. When you change the position of its pieces one or more figures vanish or reappear! Vanish puzzles are a kind of geometric paradox that involve the cutting and rearranging of a drawing. We suggest you reproduce the drawing and paste it on to a material that is easy to cut. After you have done that, cut out your puzzle along the cutting lines and go and amaze your friends! However, can you figure out how it works?

ADDING UP
Look at the picture. How many points do the dice add up to? Eight? Are you sure?

TWIN MAZES
Find the shortest path to go to C1 from A15. You have to follow simultaneously the same path in both labyrinths and you cannot cross either the lakes or the mountains.

MENTAL ARITHMETIC
Count mentally only the diagonal bird tracks and determine their exact number: are there
32, 33, or 34 bird footprints in the snow?

DIAGONALS
Is the colored shape divided by clear or by dark diagonals?

PASTA STILL LIFE
Which color is the border of the plate – A, B, or C? Is the circular decorative line best represented by color 1, color 2 or color 3?

1 2 3

A B C

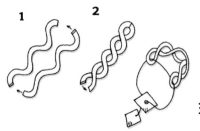

1

2

3

TORQUATO PUZZLE

To make this puzzle you need: one thin cardboard sheet, string 10–12 ins long, and two strong square cardboard pieces (approx. two x two ins). Copy the two models and paste them on to a thin cardboard sheet, then cut the pieces out. Following the three steps outlined in fig. 1 to fig. 3, you should be able to assemble this puzzle without any problem. Note one of the square cardboard pieces has a hole in it.

The aim of this intriguing puzzle is to separate the string from the bracelet without folding or tearing up the square cardboard pieces or the braided paper puzzle. Once you have freed the string, try to reassemble the puzzle.

COLOR YIN YANG
Is each semicircular shape in the yin and yang symbols the same color as its opposite symbol?

DISTORTED LEGS
Are the legs of these gentlemen bowed or
straight?

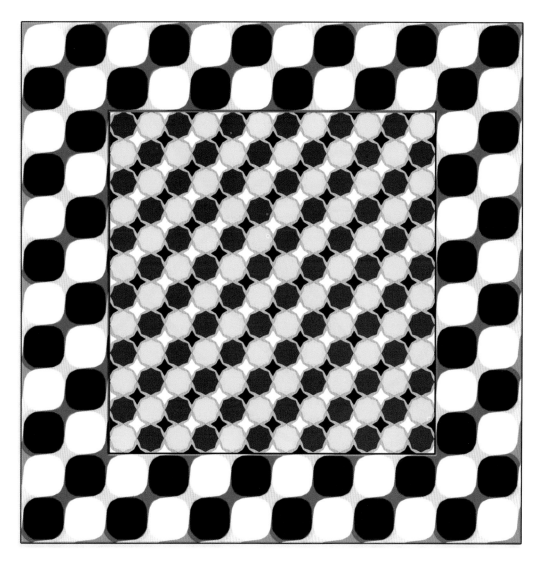

DISTORTED SQUARE
Is this square slanted?

UNDISRUPTED SKETCH
Draw a continuous line without lifting your pencil in order
to reproduce this pattern.

THE WISE PIRATE

The famous pirate Blackbeard says to his crew: "Arrr, after a long and profitable trip we now have a treasure of 396 gold pieces to share. You know that we have to divide our booty according to the Iron Pirates' Law. Each of us shall indicate the way he intends to share it out, while the others vote for or against. If the number of pirates who like the division is equal to or greater than the others who do not like it, then we will share the booty as suggested by the proposer. I start; here is my proposal..." Note that:
a) there are only 11 pirates left; b) the proposer of the idea cannot vote; c) once the vote is accepted by most voters, no pirate, not even Blackbeard, can oppose it; and d) Blackbeard is a greedy and very, very smart pirate...

Guess how many gold pieces Blackbeard will receive?

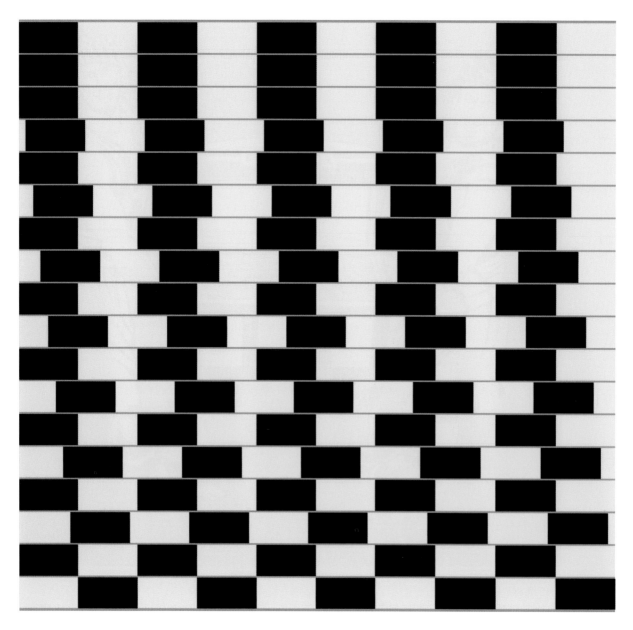

CHECKERED ROWS
Have a look at the picture consisting of alternating rows of yellow and black bricks. Are they all parallel?

SQUARING FISH
Copy the picture and cut the body of the fishes into six pieces, then rearrange them to form a perfect square. The pieces must fit together perfectly.

MISALIGNED EDGES
Which one of these three shelves has an edge that could be
a continuation of one of the edges of the single shelf?

THE STRANGEST HORSE RACE

It is summer and there is a fair in Utopialand with a horse race. The strange rule of the race is that whoever has the slowest horse wins. Two gentlemen ride with their horses to the fair and sign up for the race. When it begins they are going as slow as they can and after about two hours they have only gone about four yards. When they break for lunch, an old man walks up to the racers and gives them a suggestion. The competitors agree, so they get back on their horses and ride full speed to the finish line. Why?

COLOR ALIGNMENT
At first sight, it seems that all the red diagonals on the first straw can be continued into the green and yellow diagonals on the second and third straw respectively. Is it true?

CONCENTRIC?
Here we have two illusions in one. At first the rings do not
seem concentric, then when you move your head backwards
and forwards while staring at the center of the image some
rings seem to counter-rotate.

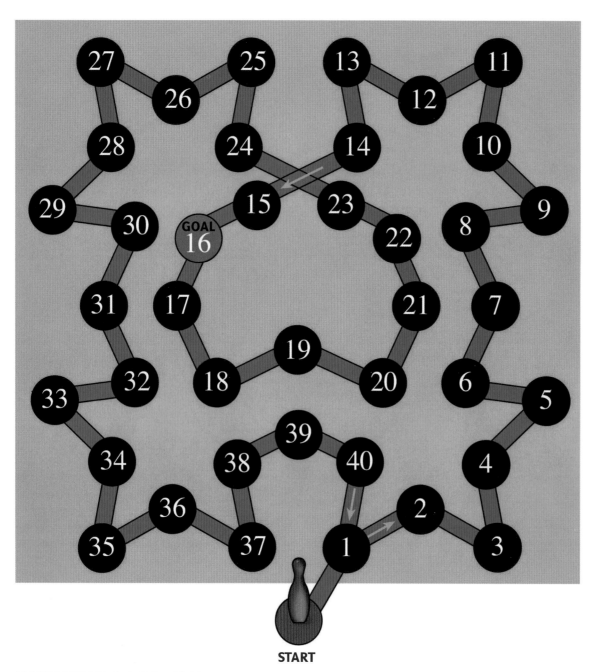

START

MATHEMATICAL GAME OF GOOSE

Throw a single die; triple the number that comes up. Starting from the red disc, move a piece by the indicated amount. Then repeat the operation until you reach the blue disc. What is the minimal number of tosses you will need to succeed in reaching your goal?

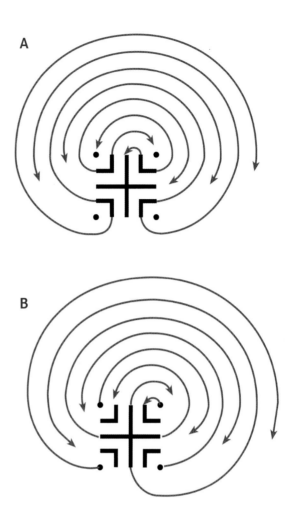

CRETAN MAZE

Mazes are universal symbols encountered in every culture. They have been used as ceremonial pathways, protective seals and traps for unwelcome spirits since the earliest days of civilization. Puzzle mazes have been exercising our feet and entertaining our brains for centuries during which time they have become a symbol of confusion.

Some antique mazes were called Cretan mazes after the isle where the mythical Minotaur was placed in a maze. All these early mazes are unicursal – that is, they contain only one continuous path and are easy to escape from, if you just follow the path. In England you can still find turf mazes based precisely upon the unicursal model associated with Greek mythology. These early labyrinths were usually constructed from a base, the heart, which is a kind of cross, as shown in the picture. Try to draw your own Cretan maze by following the illustrated instructions. Maybe can you find more than two variants!

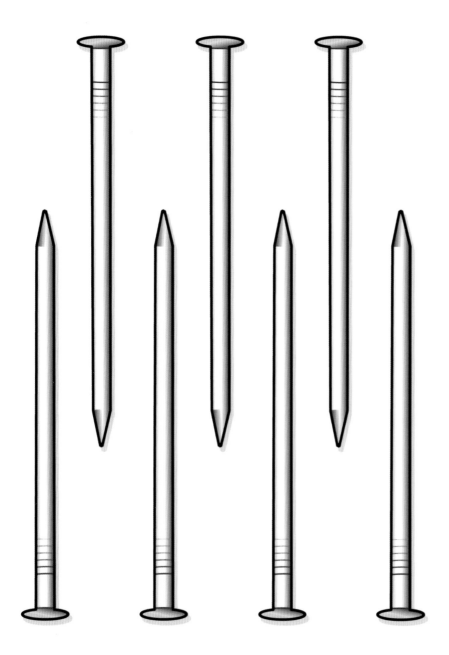

NAIL MATTER
Can you find a way to lift all seven nails off the table by using just one of them!

A

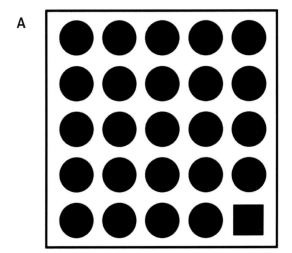

B

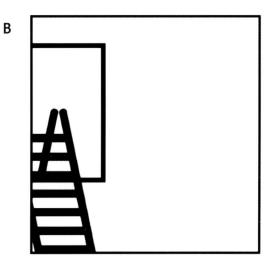

IMAGINATION TEST!
Completion figure puzzles are visual riddles that you must solve by looking carefully and by using your correlative thinking. Can you figure out what the drawings featured in figure A and figure B represent?

INTERLOCKED DISK
Is it possible to disengage the three interlocked pieces of this puzzle by only using a sliding motion?

A

B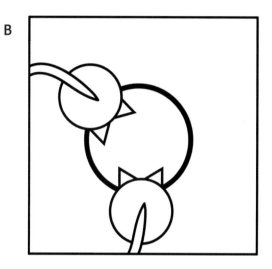

GUESS THE IMAGES
Guess what pictures A and B represent. There really is no one right answer and your guess might even be funnier than our suggested answers.

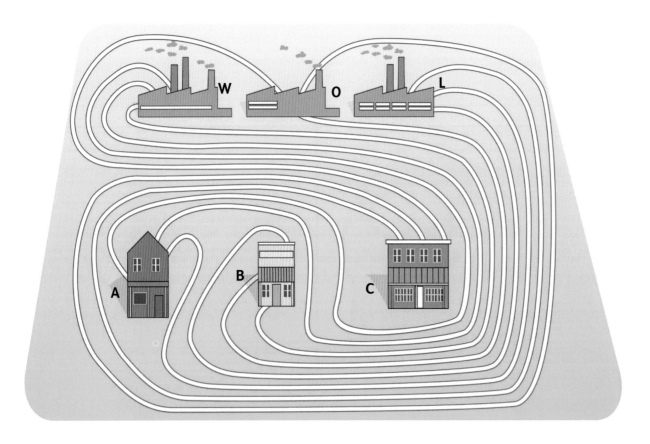

CONNECTION DILEMMA

We have laid on water, Internet connection and electricity from the utility suppliers W, O and L to each of the three houses A, B and C without any pipe crossing another. Take a pencil and check if the work has been done properly.

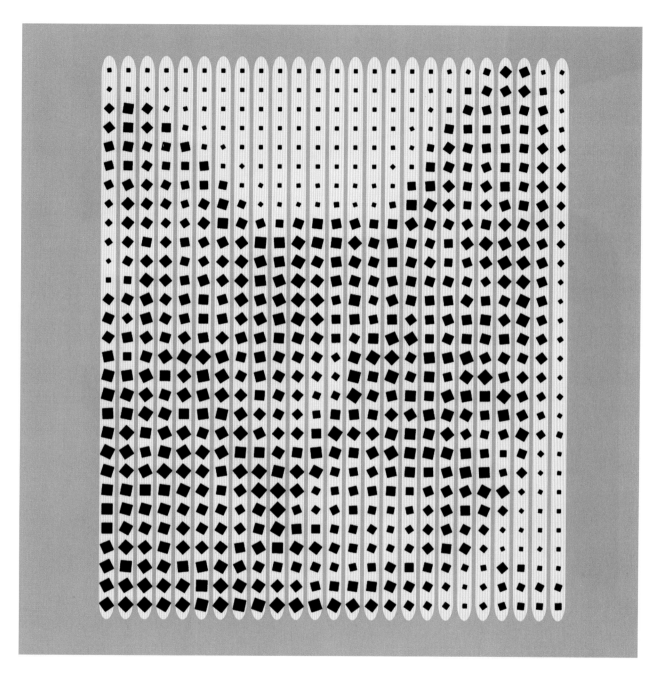

TWO IN ONE

Observe the vertical bars closely. Are they straight and parallel? Do you notice something odd? What happens if you observe the drawing from a distance of about six feet?

UNDER THE ARCHES
What's odd about this arcade?

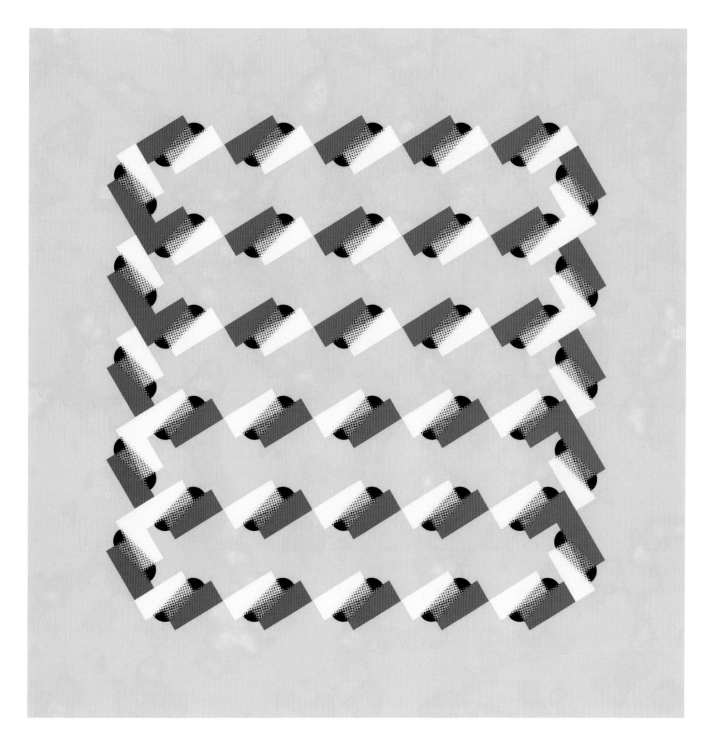

SLANTED STRUCTURE
This color structure appears at first glance to be slightly tilted to the right. Is this true?

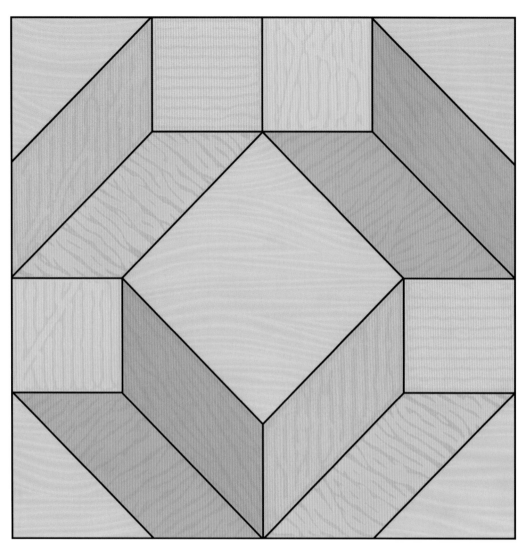

HIDDEN 3D
How many regular volumes do you perceive in this drawing?

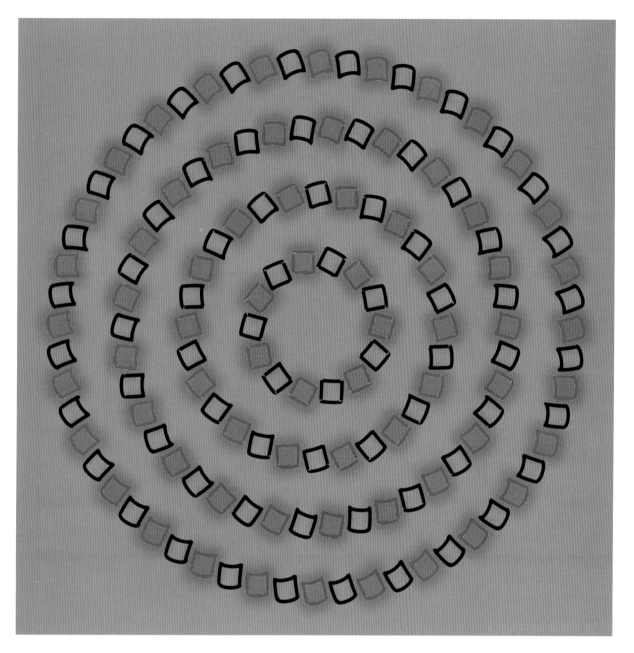

COAXIAL RINGS?
Are the circular bands of alternate red and black squares perfectly concentric to each other?

KEEP YOUR DISTANCE
Which path is longest: the path from A to B or the path from A to C?

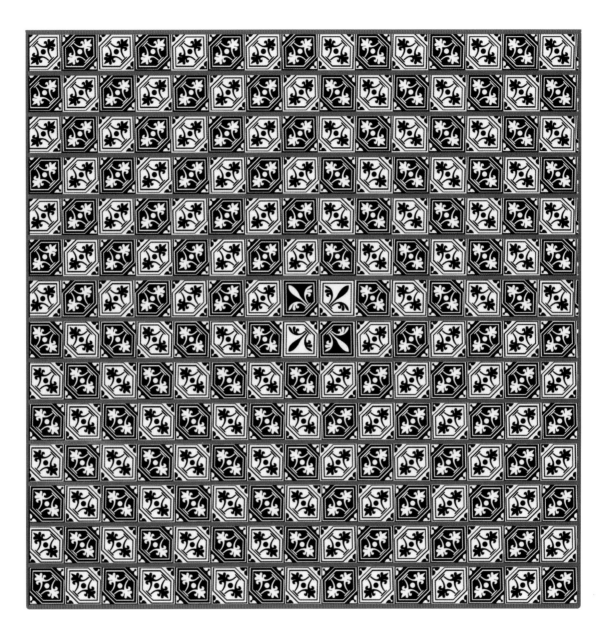

ANTIQUE TAPESTRY
In an antique shop we found this medieval tapestry containing geometric patterns that seem to bulge. The question is, are the rows curved or perfectly straight and parallel?

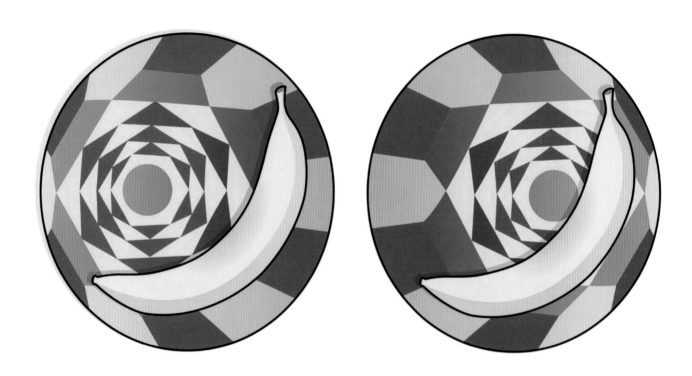

BOWLED OVER
Which object is most like a fruit bowl?

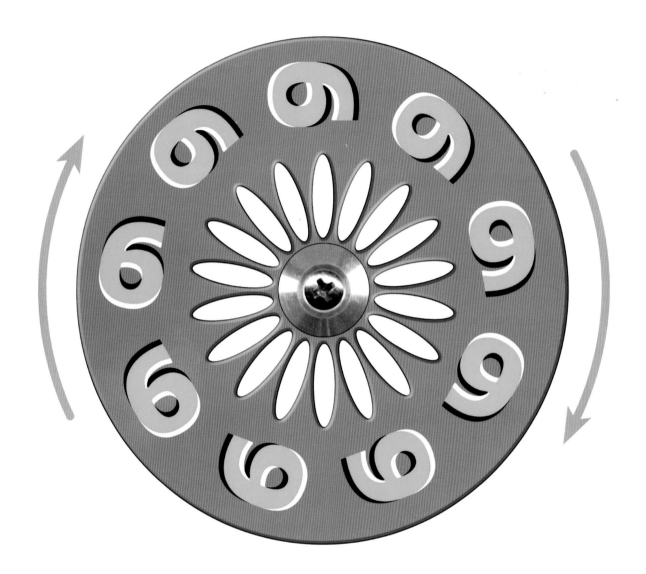

PERPETUAL MOTION?
How does this perpetual motion device work? Do you know
why the wheel looks likely to rotate slightly?

EVERGREEN?

Observe this picture from a distance. You will notice that some regions of the patterns seem darker and give the ensemble a 3D look. Can you say how many different greens the picture contains?

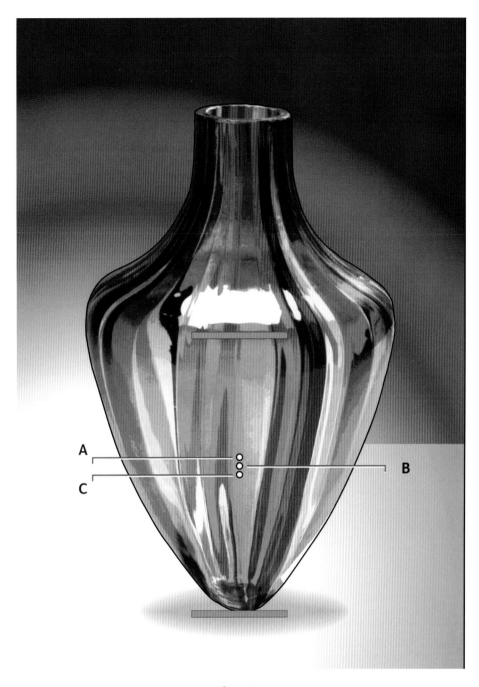

PANDORA'S VASE
Which dot is half-way up the distances between
the two blue bars: dot A, B or C?

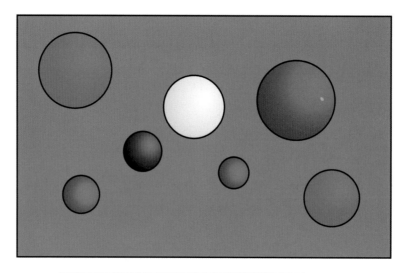

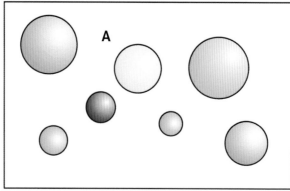

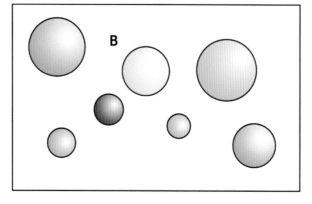

LIGHT BALLS
Which colored ball – A or B – corresponds to the
light colored ball on the dark background?

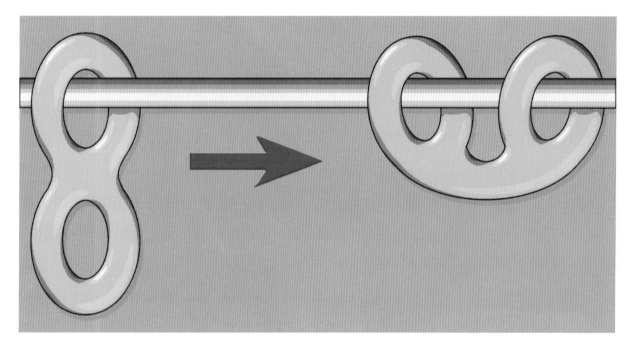

TRANSFORMATIONS
Alter the fresh eight-shaped pastry in order to thread the stick into its second loop. You cannot unthread the stick from the pastry nor cut the pastry in any way.

COME CLEAN
Are the red labels of the three soaps different sizes?

GEOMETRY

Repeating a simple geometric pattern (see the green shape) can be used to create great optical effects. The background gives the impression that it is composed of three interlinked structures with holes.

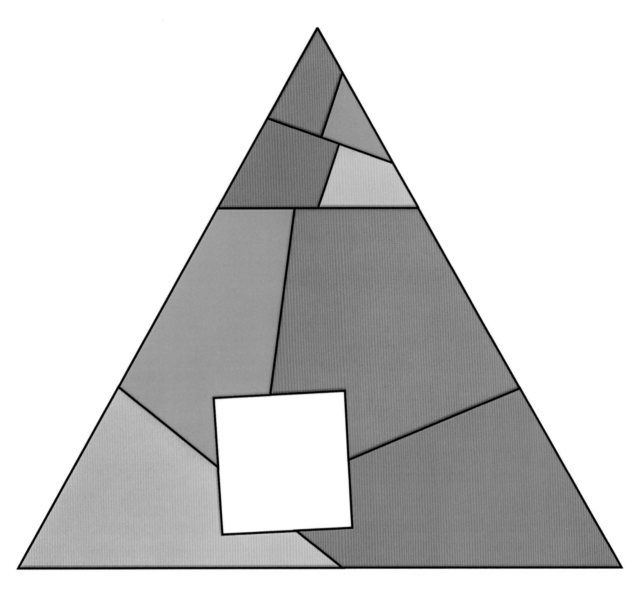

IMPERFECT TRIANGLE
The aim of the game is to restore the triangle. Reproduce
the image, cut the puzzle out and then rearrange its pieces
to form a triangle without the square hole.

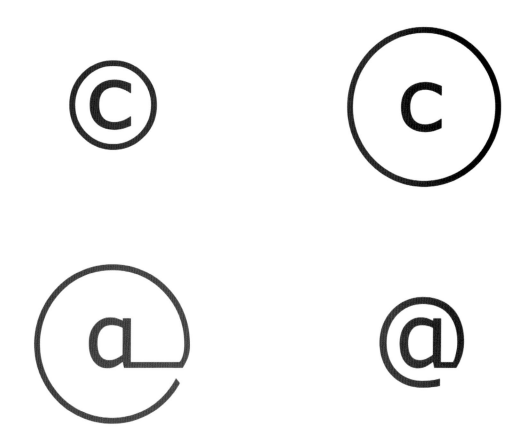

SYMBOLIC
Look at the typographical symbols. Is each pair of letters of different size? For instance, is the c in the circle on your left larger than the c in the circle on your right?

AREAS

Can you find in the upper diagram a) three shapes with the same area; b) three shapes with the same perimeter and c) two shapes with the same surface? When you have done that, look at the three colored shapes below them. What do they have in common?

MATCHMAKER
Can you take just one single match and carve it in order to represent a skier as shown in the picture?

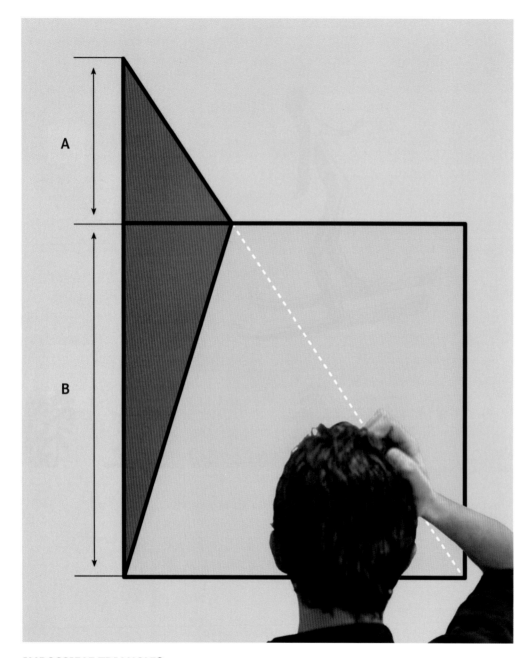

IMPOSSIBLE TRIANGLE?

If A = 2 ins and B = 5 ins, can you calculate the area of the red triangle? It might help to know the green shape represents a square.

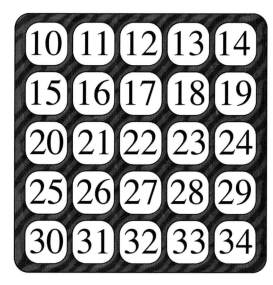
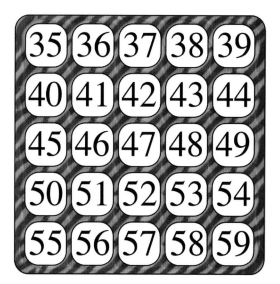

A

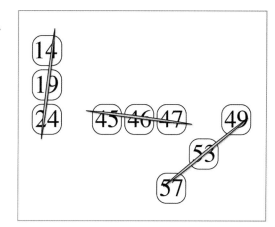

TRIADS

Ask one of your friends to cover with a toothpick three aligned numbers of the red table in any direction – vertically, horizontally or diagonally (see fig. A). Then tell them to add up the digits of the numbers until only one digit remains. For instance, if numbers 21, 22 and 23 were selected, the operation would be: 2 + 1 + 2 + 2 + 2 + 3 = 12, 1 + 2 = 3. Invite them to select three other numbers with the toothpick in the green table and to repeat the adding operation. Finally, ask them to multiply the first result by the second result and to add up the digits of the final result as previously done. Then you will correctly guess the number. What is that number and how do you know it will be correct?

THE WARRIOR AND THE TORII
A torii is a traditional Japanese gate commonly found at the entry to a shrine or to a temple. It has two upright supports, two crossbars on the top and is frequently painted red. Can you say if the torii in the picture is well built? Do you see one warrior or two warriors in the scenery?

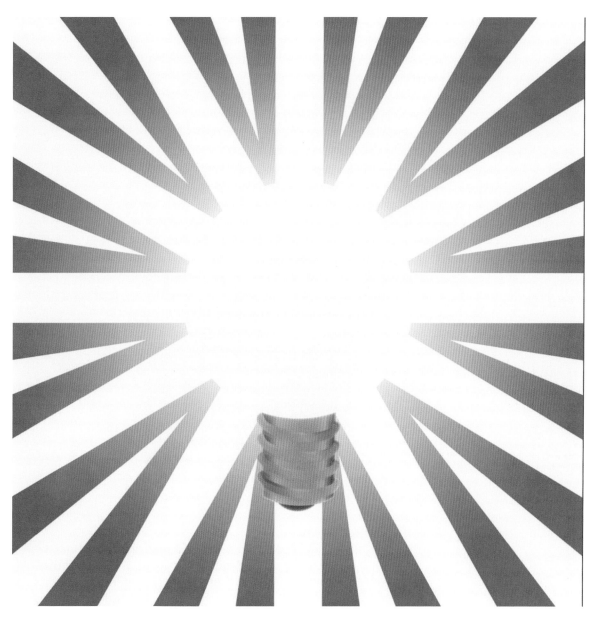

LIGHT BULB ILLUSION
Is the central yellow color of the image darker than (or different from) its surround? While staring at the center of the image, move closer to and further from the page. What happens?

THE MAGIC DOLLAR

Three students checked into a hotel and paid the receptionist $195 for a single and a double room ($65 each). When the hotel manager returned, he noticed that the clerk had incorrectly charged $195 instead of $170 for the rooms. The manager told the clerk to return $25 to the students. The clerk, knowing that the students would not be able to divide $25 evenly, decided to keep $13 and to give them only $12.

The students were happy because they paid only $195 − $12 = $183 for the room ($61 each). However, if they paid $61 and the blameworthy clerk kept $13, that totals $196! Where does the other dollar come from?

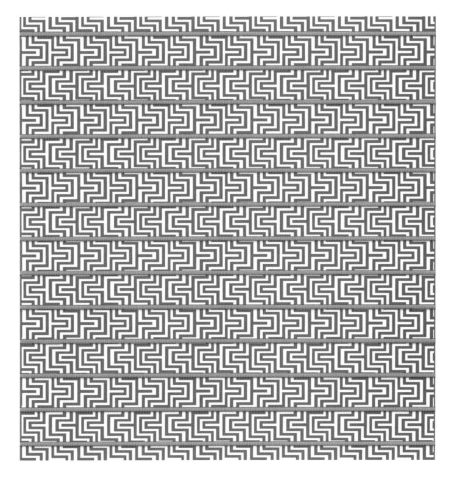

STRAIGHT OR NOT?
Do the orange lines diverge or are they slightly bowed?

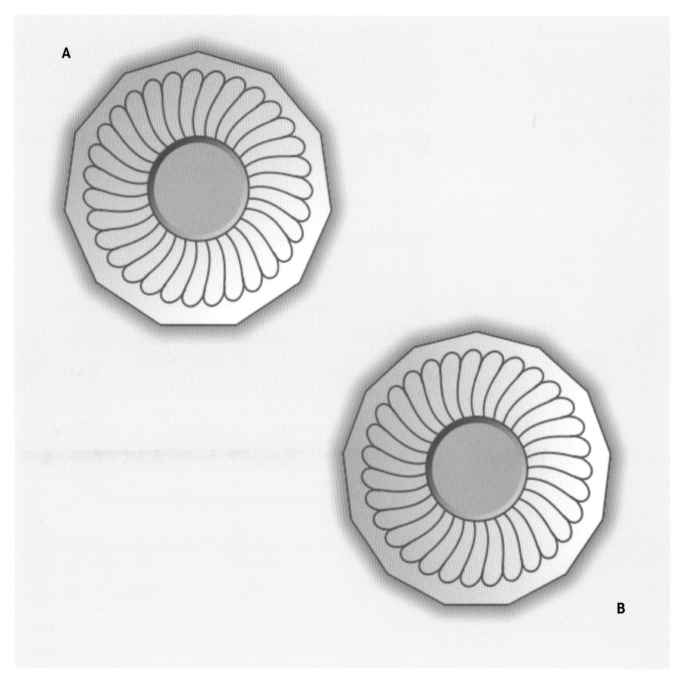

OBSERVATION TEST
Can you find three tiny differences between pictures A and B?

VISUAL PATIENCE TEST

The image represents an antique unicursal labyrinth. Take a pencil and exit the labyrinth starting from the red dot. This is just a patience test – there's no answer! If you can complete it without taking a handful of tranquilizers, it confirms that you are a person with a very cool temperament.

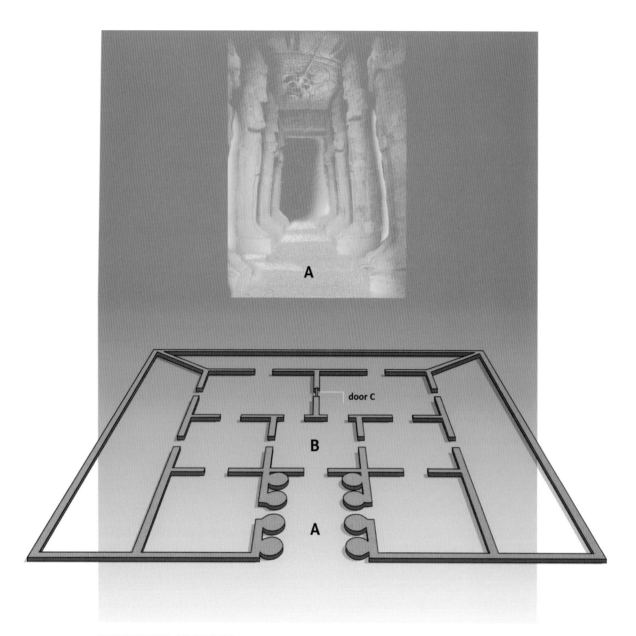

THE TEMPLE OF HORUS

You have discovered the lost temple of Horus and now you have to visit its rooms going through all the open doors once. A represents your departure point and the B your arrival point. When you have finished your visiting, with your imagination open door C and try visit the rooms in the temple again respecting, the initial challenge of going through all the open doors once.

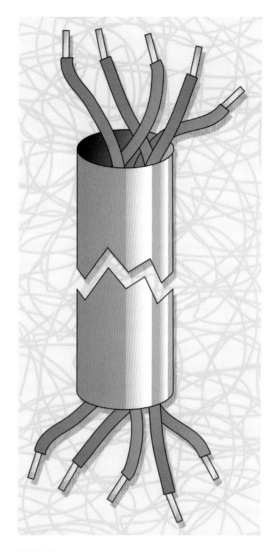

WIRED

You have to set up an electric network of five individual wires in a house. Connection one of the second floor has to be connected with connection one of the ground floor; likewise with connections two, three, four and five. How do you know which end of each wire corresponds to the other one? You can check the wires by going down to the ground floor once. You may use a battery, a light bulb, a pencil and ten self-stick labels to help you.

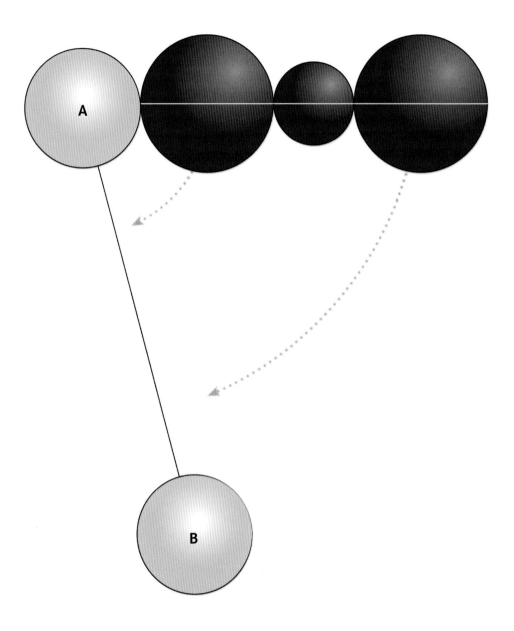

SIZE DISTORTION
If you make the alignment of three purple balls turn around the yellow ball A (as shown in the image) do you think it will pass between balls A and B without shifting ball B?

TO THE POINT
How many arrows can you see in this picture?

DISTORTED BOARD
This is an elegant version of the Fraser illusion. The concentric marquetry elements within the checkerboard center seem slanted, but they are in fact perfectly straight and at right angles!

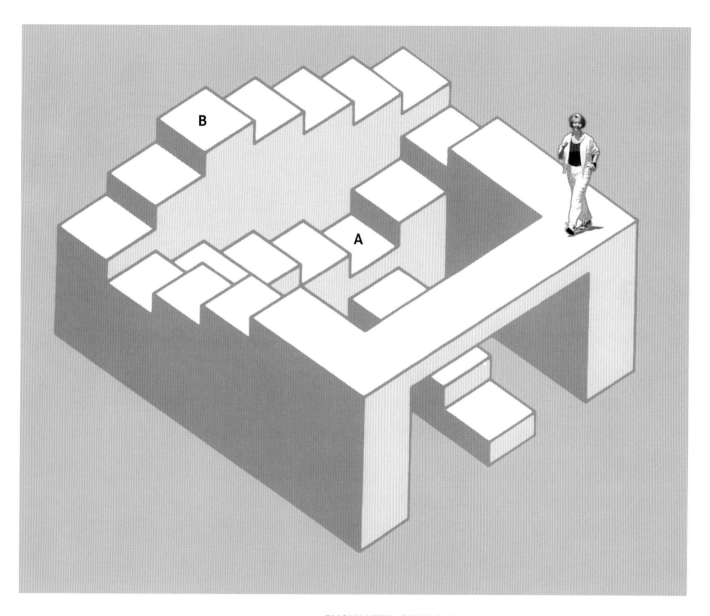

ENCHANTED STAIRCASE
Starting from A and going directly to B, the jogging woman will climb the same amount of steps whether she goes to the left or to the right side! However, if she decided to go from A to B by crossing the bridge something odd happens. Can you guess what?

MAGIC MIRRORS

Observe both katoptrons (antique Greek mirrors) A and B. Katoptron B is the mirror image of katoptron A. Can you find what their fundamental difference is?

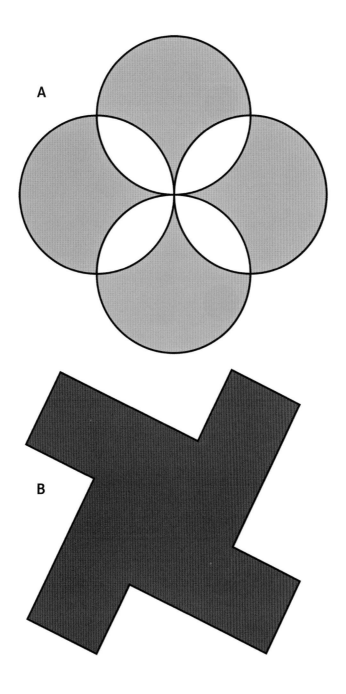

A

B

A QUESTION OF GEOMETRY
Can you prove empirically – without measuring or
superimposing any shape on the other one – that the area
of curvilinear shape A equals that of the area of cross-
shaped figure B?

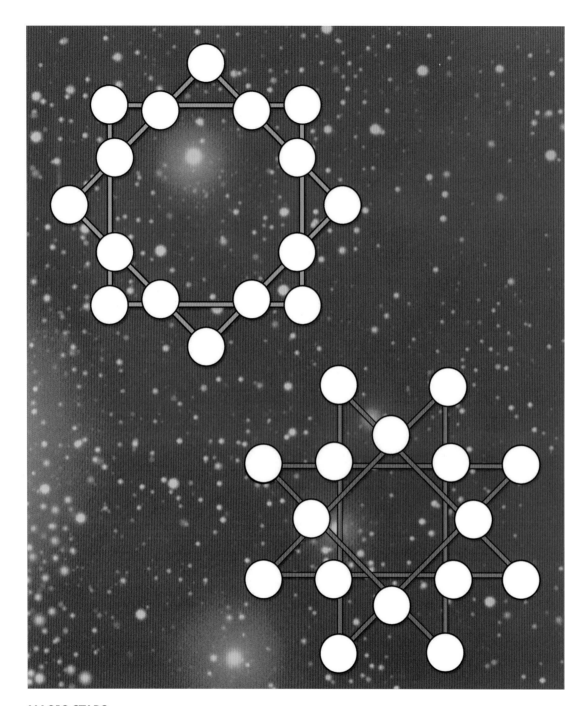

MAGIC STARS

Find a simple, calculation-free method to arrange numbers from one to 16 at the nodes of both magic octagrams so that the constant sum of the numbers in every line is 34.

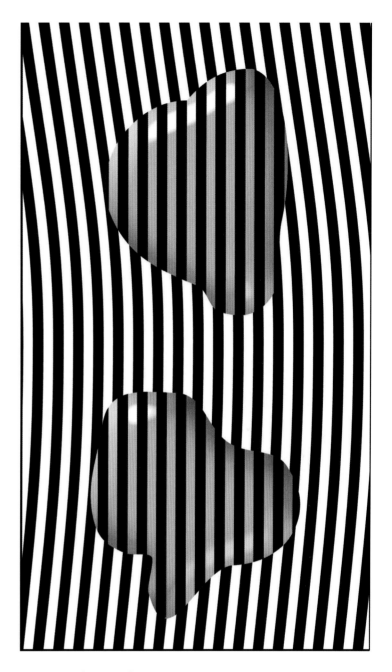

WATER DROP EFFECT
Are the lines within the water drops colinear to the page or are they slightly tilted?

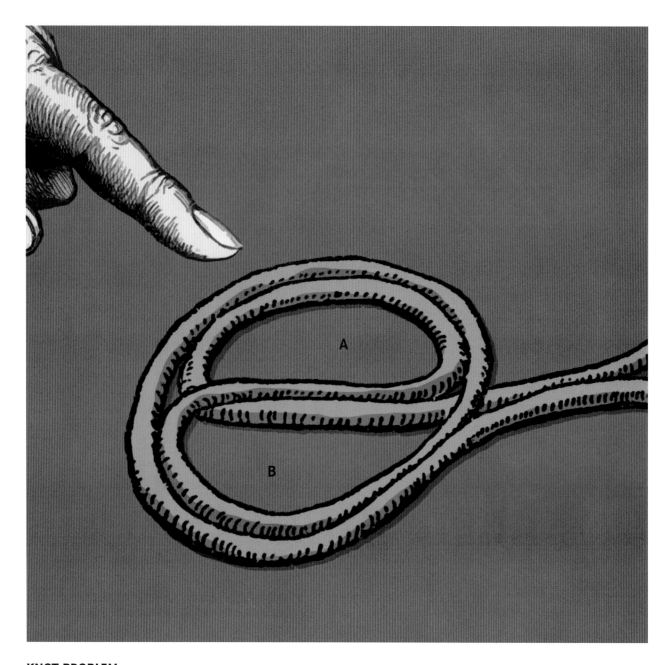

KNOT PROBLEM
In which of the loops – A or B – would your finger be gripped
if we pull the string's ends while it was inside?

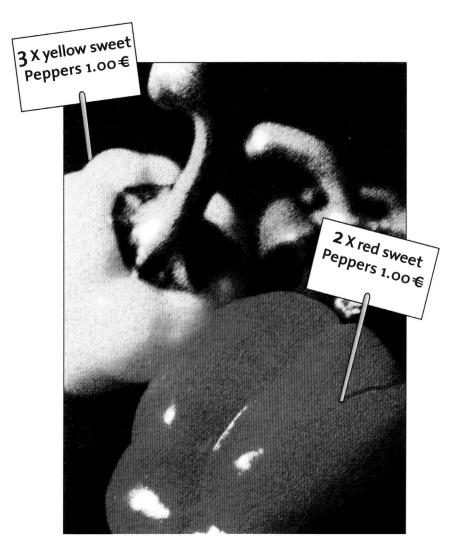

3 X yellow sweet Peppers 1.00 €

2 X red sweet Peppers 1.00 €

RED PEPPER YELLOW PEPPER
A greengrocer on my street received 30 red and 30 yellow sweet peppers from his wholesaler. The recommended prices were one euro for two red sweet peppers and one euro for two yellow sweet peppers. To avoid color disparity he decided to sell five sweet peppers for two euros. He thought that there was no difference between selling five sweet peppers for two euros and selling three for one euro and two for one. He sold all the vegetables and earned 24 euros – one euro less than expected. Can you explain why?

THE FOOTPRINT ILLUSION
Are the footprints embossed?

CLASSIC ILLUSION
This is a simplified Münsterberg illusion to demonstrate that even simple regular shapes can induce important visual distortions. Most of these illusions are caused by conflicting local and global image features.

MAGIC MAGIC SQUARE

Here is an incredible self-working magic trick. Take a sheet of paper about nine inches square. Fold the sheet in half four times so that the folds make a four-by-four grid of cells. Open out the sheet and make the folds clear and precise.

Write out the following numbers: 1, 15, 14, 4, 12, 6, 7, 9, 8, 10, 11, 5, 13, 3, 2, and 6 in the cells formed by the folds from left to right. Take a pair of scissors and carefully cut along the folds in any one direction, providing only that you do not detach any portion of the sheet (as shown in fig. A).

Now start folding the sections of the sheet together (along the folds already made, see fig. B). Try to make the folding as random and convoluted as you can. For example, you can place folds inside folds if you like. Do this until the sheet is folded into a packet the size of a single cell (fig. C). Take the scissors and carefully trim the edges of the packet (fig. D) so that all the cells are now separated.

Deal the cells out on to the table. You will notice that some of the numbers are face-up and others are face-down, as determined by your random pattern of cutting and folding. Now count up the total of the face-up numbers and divide this total by two.

Do you know what the total will be?

LEANING TOWER PAINTINGS
Which of these paintings hangs slightly askew?

HYPNOTIC SNOW EFFECT
This is a form of Ouchi illusion. The blue disc seems to vibrate and float over the radial background. If you concentrate on the disc you may perceive a subtle TV "snow" effect. For some people, this illusion can also be used as an effective anti-stress device. Try it!

THE RED SPOT
Make a large red spot on a page and find a trick that allows you to trace a line within its edges that is approximately twice the perimeter of the page sheet without lifting your pen or repeating the same path! You can cut the page twice, but you cannot detach any piece of paper.

ANTIQUE MAGIC SQUARE

Magic squares have fascinated people for centuries. They are formed by filling in all the squares with numbers starting from one so that the sum – called the magic constant – of each row, column, and diagonal is the same. The construction of magic squares is an amusement of great antiquity. Magic squares were known in India and China before the Christian era. Several sources say the Chinese constructed three-by-three magic squares circa 500 BC.

Can you make a magic square? Try to fill the checked square with numbers from 1 to 16, so that when you sum these numbers (vertically, horizontally and diagonally) you obtain 34. Can you find a trick to solve this problem easily?

A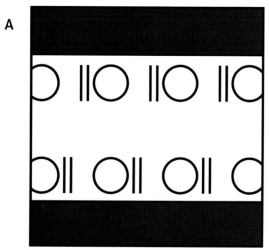

B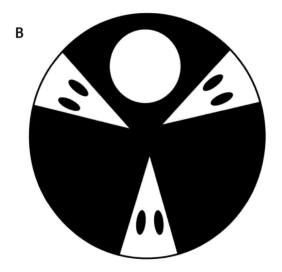

MORE GUESS THE IMAGES
Can you figure out what pictures A and B represent? Use your correlative thinking!

TO SHAVE OR NOT TO SHAVE

Imagine that a barber in a small town puts up a sign in the shop that reads "I shave all those men, and only those men, who do not shave themselves." We can then divide the males in this town into two groups, those who shave themselves and those who are shaved by the barber. To which group does the barber himself belong? Can you find an original way to solve this paradox?

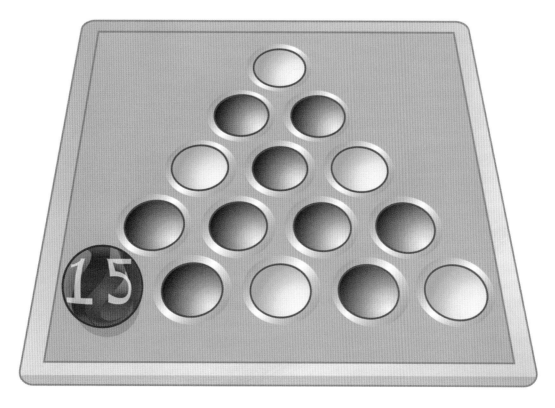

TRIANGULAR DIFFERENCES

Complete the puzzle by placing each numbered marble on a hole, following the rule that the number of the marble placed on a black hole should be the numerical difference of those placed on the adjacent blue holes. The marble number 15 is already placed on a blue hole.

DIVERGING SLATS
Are the vertical slats perfectly parallel?

MIND CONTROL
Here is a tough mission for you... Can you control your mind by not thinking of a red fish for five minutes?

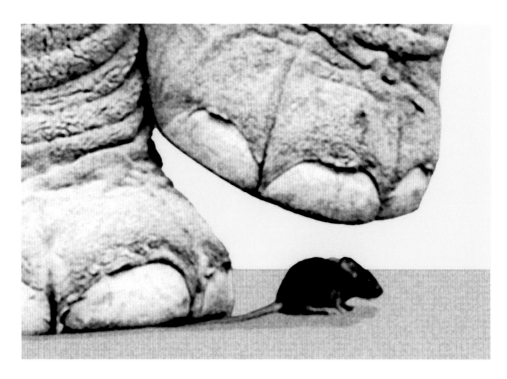

THE GREAT ELEPHANT DILEMMA
An argumentative elephant captures a mouse and promises that it will not squash the mouse provided it can tell in advance what the elephant is going to do. The mouse replies "You will squash me."

What should the elephant do?

OBSERVATION TEST
Can you guess what induces a visual distortion in the checkerboard?

TRIANGULAR KANGAROO

Reproduce and cut out the outline of the kangaroo. Then cut this paper marsupial into three pieces with just two straight cuts, so that the pieces may be put together to form an equilateral triangle. No overlapping allowed!

THE ILLUSIVE LABYRINTH
Can you a) find the path to free the red dot from
the maze and b) draw a line to join together the
small orange squares marked with an x?

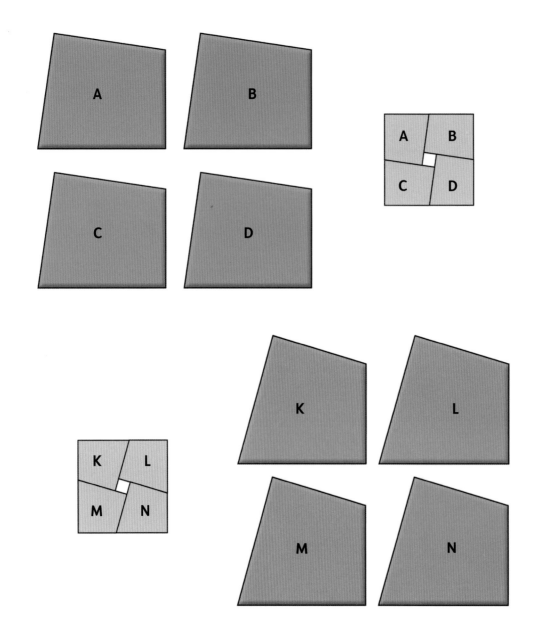

FOUR-PIECE PUZZLES

This is a two-player puzzle. Copy the puzzle and take the puzzle pieces of 1 for you and give the pieces of puzzle 2 to a friend. It is important to notice that all the pieces have exactly the same area. Now each of you has to form a square as illustrated (starting position). The challenge is to rearrange the pieces in order to form another square without the hole in the middle. Who will win first? Why?

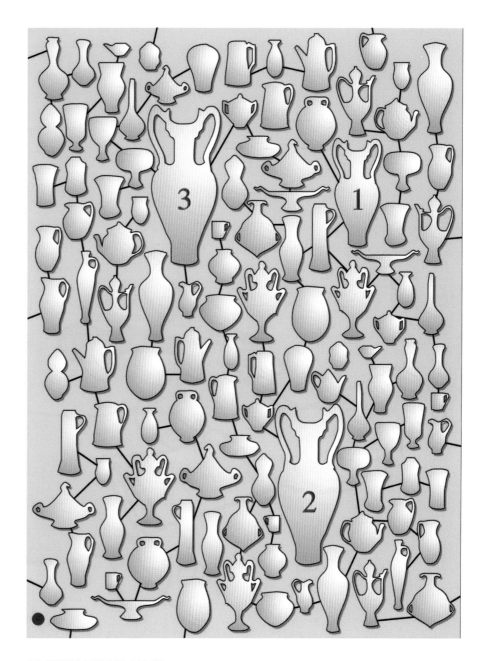

ARCHEOLOGICAL MAZE
Starting from the red spot, trace your way through the antique vases in order to arrive first at the large amphora vase numbered one. Then make your way to vase two and finally to vase three before returning to the red point. You cannot use the same path or path-junctions twice.

THE THREE-TAILED DOG
a) No dog has two tails.
b) Every dog has one more tail than no dog –
Therefore... Every dog has two + one = three tails!

What is wrong with the above reasoning?

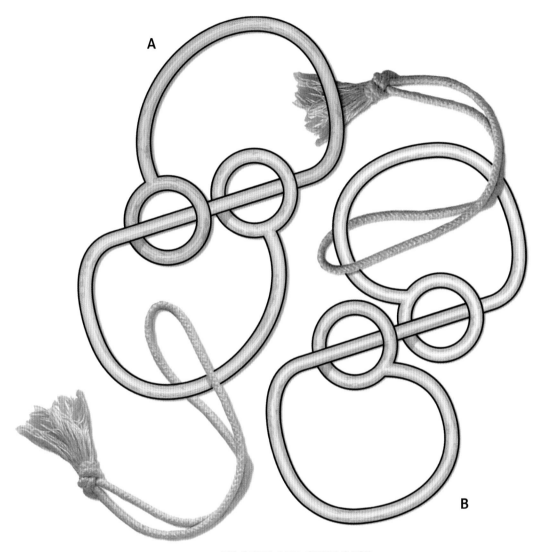

A

B

AN OPEN AND SHUT CASE
Visually, the loops of the two wire puzzles depicted above
seem closed. However, it is possible to free the circular
string from one of them. Which one?

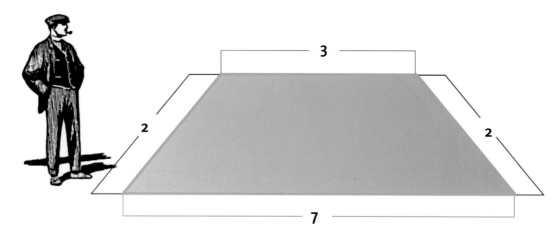

A QUESTION OF DISTANCE
What is the area of George's plot estimated in square miles?

ANOTHER QUESTION OF AREA
If the area of the warning sign is 100 square inches, what is the area of the central white equilateral triangle?

AREA AGAIN
If the diameter of the dial is four inches, what is the distance (red diagonal) that separates the hands of the turnip watch?

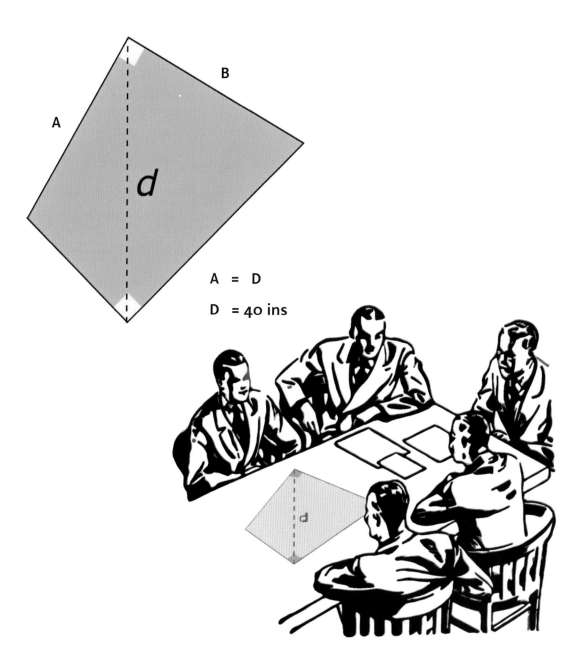

A

B

d

A = D

D = 40 ins

ENOUGH INFORMATION?
Knowing that the quadrilateral has two right angles and two adjacent sides that are equal, calculate its area. Is this impossible?

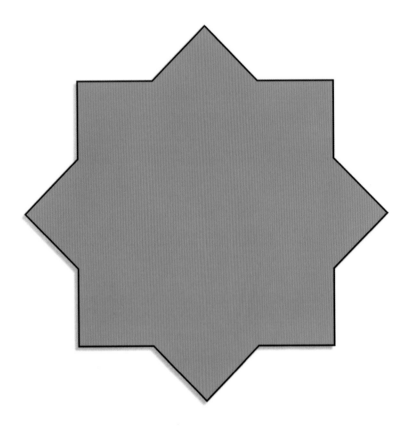

STAR TRANSFORMATION
Copy the geometric shape and cut it so that its pieces can
be assembled to form a square.

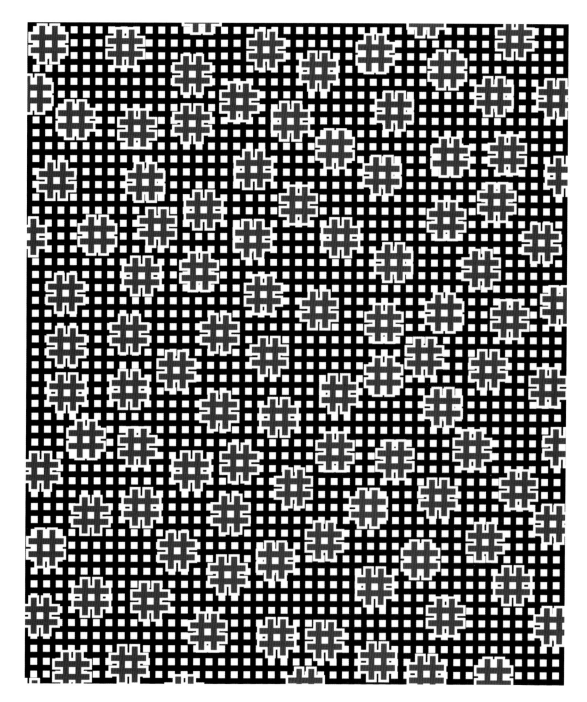

ANOTHER OBSERVATION TEST

Look at the picture for a while. Then how many kinds of blue patterns can you discern in the drawing?

I HAD A DREAM

Gandabbar the elf, being superstitious, is convinced he has dreamt the winning lottery numbers. Unfortunately, the dream was a bit vague.

"Tell me about it" said his friend Leto the goblin.

"There were 88 doors guarded by 88 guards and a voice asked them to open or close the doors in a precise order."

"Which is?"

"First the voice said 'Open all the doors of the Kingdom' and the guards obeyed. Then the voice said 'Every other guard, close their door' and then 'Now every third guard open their door if it is closed or close it if it is open.'"

"What do you mean every third guard?" asked Leto.

"Well" said Gandabbar, "The first two guards stand firm and the third one obeys and then the sixth, the ninth, the twelfth and so on."

"I will bet the voice continued up to number 88 with the same order" said Leto.

"Exactly!" exclaimed Gandabbar. "It concluded saying 'the doors remaining open and having a two digit number, will bring you wealth.' How can I discover what numbers they are?"

"There are two ways" answered Let. "By long calculation or by using your brain."

Do you know how to discover the six winning numbers from the dream?

Answers

MAGIC WARDROBE, page 20

The green line CD seems clearly shorter than AB formed by the two walls, but in fact they are perfectly equal. This illusion is related to the Müller–Lyer illusion and the picture is from the end of the 1800s.

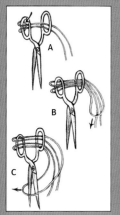

THE GREAT ESCAPE, page 21

The way to do it is to loosen the loop knot (figure a) and pull it through the opposite finger hole (fig. b). Then, pass this loop all the way over the scissors (fig. c). Do not twist it around. Finally, by pulling on the other end of the loop string you will be able to free the scissor. Now you know how it is done you can challenge a friend to remove the scissors without cutting the string!

ZEN THOUGHTS, page 22

Draw a longer line next to the first one. The first line is now definitely shorter...

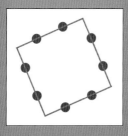

BOX CLEVER, page 23

It is a simple perception puzzle, but the angle of slope of the whole figure makes it a little bit difficult. See drawing.

PERFECT TOP HAT, page 24

No. If you measure them with a ruler you will see that the exact opposite is true – the height CD of the hat is slightly less than the width AB. If you don't believe it... take a ruler and verify it for yourself! It is an interesting version of the Müller-Lyer illusion.

SWISS CROSS, page 25

See illustration.

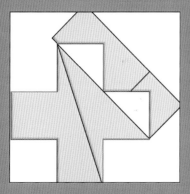

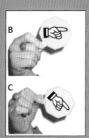

GIVING DIRECTIONS, page 26

To understand why the fingers point to an apparently unexpected direction, you have to consider that the rackets in B and C use two symmetry axes instead of one – the vertical axis of the person who holds the racket and the axis of the handle of the racket.

TIED UP, page 27

C. The squares are alternately bright and dark. The effect that induced you to choose A instead of C is called simultaneous color contrast.

MAGIC PROBABILITIES, page 28

Under certain conditions, if you switch your choice at each game. in the long run you will win two times out of three. Here is why...

On the table there are three cards – a King of Spades, a not-King of Spades card one, and a not-King of Spades card two.

If we assume the host of the game knows where the King of Spades is and you know that the game host knows where the King of Spades is, the chance of winning is doubled when you switch to the other playing (card A) rather than sticking with your original choice (card C), because the game host deliberately turned a not-King of Spades card over.

At the point where you are asked whether to switch there are three possible situations corresponding to your initial choice, each with equal probability (1/3):
a) You originally picked the playing card hiding not-King of Spades card one. The game host has deliberately shown the other not-King of Spades card two.
b) You originally picked the playing card hiding not-King of Spades card two. The game host has deliberately shown the other not-King of Spades card one.
c) You originally picked the playing card hiding the King of Spades. The game host has shown either of the two not-King of Spades cards.

If you choose to switch, you win in the first two cases. A player choosing to stay with the initial choice wins in only the third case. Since in two out of three equally likely cases switching wins, the odds of winning by switching are 2/3. In other words, a player who has a policy of always switching will win on average two times out of three.

If we assume the game host doesn't really know where the King of Spades is and you know that the game host doesn't know where the King of Spades is, then when the game host turns the not-King of Spades card over, the probability that you originally picked the King of Spades increases from 1/3 to 1/2. The odds are in this case equal, whether you switch your initial choice or not.

If we assume you do not really know whether the game host knows where the King of Spades is or not, the probability that you originally picked the King of Spades is then included between 1/3 and 1/2. Switching in this case is still advantageous, your odds ratio being ranged between 1/2 and 2/3.

The Paradox of Bertrand's Box

A similar probability puzzle was published by the mathematician Joseph Bertrand in his 1889 text Calcul des Probabilités. The reader is asked to imagine three desks each with two drawers. He knows that one desk contains a gold medal in each drawer, one contains a silver medal in each drawer and one contains one of each. He doesn't know which desk is which. The question posed was: "If the reader opens a drawer and discovers a gold medal, what are the chances that the other drawer on that desk also contains gold?"
A well-known adaptation of this puzzle is the 'Monty Hall problem'.

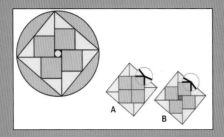

QUIRINUS PUZZLE, page 29

Yes, it is possible, but there is a trick. The large square inscribed in the disc is not really a square but a slightly concave regular shape (see fig. A). When you fit the small disk into the large disc the apparent large square becomes slightly convex (fig. B). This is a neat form of geometric optical illusion.

SHAPESHIFTER, page 30

You can make four regular convex polygons and four regular concave polygons.

CONVERGING OR DIVERGING?, page 31

Yes, the rays converge perfectly in the center of the disc. This is another version of the famous Fraser illusion.

ARCHIMEDES LOGO, page 32

See the diagram (left).

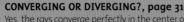

SWITCHED ON, page 33

Turn the red switch for five minutes. Turn it off and turn on the blue switch. Open the door:
– if the light is on, it is the blue switch;
– if the light is off touch the light bulb; if the bulb is hot, it is the red switch;
– if the light is off and cold, it is the green switch.

CHAINED, page 34

See the diagram (left).

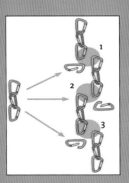

FILL IN, page 35

Hulk or G.I.? Neither, rather an intellectual snob as you can see from the drawing.

MEMORY TEST, page 36

Interestingly, most people draw the pattern shown in fig. B (instead of the original pattern in fig. A).

MATHEMATICAL MIND-READING, page 37

Did you notice that the first black or red listed numbers (called key numbers) are only on one single card? Numbers one and two are only on the purple card, three and six on the blue card, nine and 18, on the yellow card and, finally, 27 and 54 on the gray card. All the other remaining numbers are combinations of those key numbers! For instance, number 42 is red on the blue card (whose first red number is six), black on the yellow card (whose first black number is nine) and red again on the gray card (whose first red number is 27). Adding up six + nine + 27 we magically obtain the number 42! Similar magic games using powers of two as key numbers were familiar in the past.

ROUND-TRIP, page 38

This is a tricky puzzle. Most people will answer 100 miles/hour. However, the actual answer is 96 miles/hour instead! Why? Because you have to consider the TIME spent to cover these distances. Let us say that the distance covered from A to B is 80 miles/hour x three hours = 240 miles; then to travel from B to A takes 240 miles. At 120 miles/hour it takes two hours. If we divide this distance by the average time spent to cover it (3 hours plus 2 hours divided by 2 equals 2.5 hours), we obtain 240 miles divided by 2.5 hours; that equals an average of 96 miles/hour. Meaning the total amount of time for the trip is the same as if you travelled the entire trip at 96 miles per hour. In mathematics, such an average is called harmonic mean and it is used in electronics to calculate the mean resistance of two or more resistors connected in parallel.

ROUND AND ROUND, page 39

The perimeter of the triangular wheel A corresponds to 2d x Pi / 2, (see left) simplified in d x Pi which is the same as the normal wheel B! Therefore by pedalling the same number of turns, we cover the same distances using either wheel A or B. The particular geometric shape of the wheel A is called the Reuleaux triangle.
To have a comfortable ride, you have to attach a fixed disc with a circular sliding channel to the fork of your bike, as shown in the example.

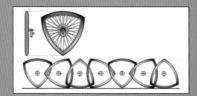

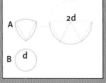

CAN YOU SEE IT?, page 40

Hold the edge of the book up flat to your eye and look across the page; you will see the word CACHE in block capitals This kind of visual puzzle is called an anamorphic image. A lot of great artists during the Renaissance used this effect to create strange illusions.

ROYAL COURT, page 41

See image (left). The famous Swiss mathematician Euler posed a similar question – the Problem of the 36 Officers. Is it possible to line up 36 officers, each with one of six ranks and belonging to one of six regiments, in a six by six square, so each row and column contains one officer of each rank and one from each regiment? The problem is insoluble, but try it out with cards instead of policemen!

SQUARED, page 42

See the image (right) and follow the instructions.

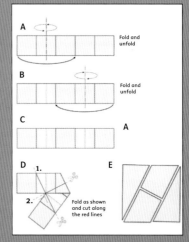

MAGIC PATH PROBLEM, page 43
See image (left).

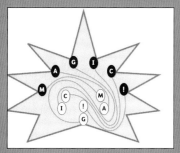

TRIANGLES TO SQUARE, page 44
See the image.

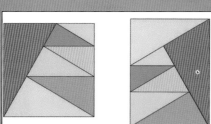

IMAGE TESTS, page 45

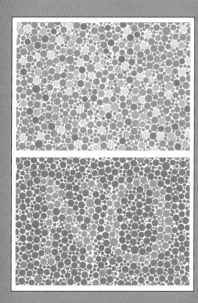

This is an interesting test to detect color deficiency based on the Ishihara plates. If you can see only the letters S I you have normal vision. However, if you can read 'N O' in the lower image you can see how an individual affected with color deficiency sees it and you may be affected by color deficiency. Color deficiency is a condition in which certain colors cannot be distinguished. It is usually an inherited condition. About eight percent of men suffer from it, though fewer women have some form of color deficiency. Red/green color deficiency is by far the most common form of the problem with almost 99% of sufferers having problems in distinguishing reds and greens. Blue/yellow color deficiency also exists, but is rare and there is no commonly available test for it. There is no treatment for color deficiency, nor is it usually the cause of any significant disability. In certain cases, color deficiency can be an advantage. A person with color deficiency is able to better discriminate camouflages than someone with a normal vision. Color blindness is used colloquially instead of color deficiency, but it is an inaccurate term.

HOW LONG?, page 46
This illusion is based on the Müller-Lyer optical illusion and is mainly due to the 'V' shapes that enclose the lines like brackets.

CHINOISERIES, page 47
The man in the foreground is approximately 15% taller than the man in the background.

THE RIGHT ANGLE, page 48
Due to a trick of the apparent perspective, the 90-degree angle doesn't look very convincing (see left), so take a set square and verify it!

COLOR CURVE, page 49
If we could slide the rectangles as shown in the examples we would see that the curvilinear shapes are actually all of the same shade! This illusion is related to the Benussi ring illusion and is mainly due to the lateral inhibition of our visual system.

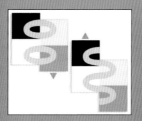

CASH CONUNDRUM, page 50

The one cent! The solution is very different to that expected. This is to illustrate the difficulty to determine at a rough guess the real size of circular objects. Psychologically we tend to see circular objects smaller than they appear in reality. You may perform this experiment on your friends using real coins (the stack is made up of 10 coins of one cent).

DOME DILEMMA, page 51
It seems incredible, but the dome is actually gray. The answer is C and D! The dark surrounding color influences the neutral color of the dome. This effect is called contrast of color.

DISTORTED LINES, page 52
The pair of lines A, despite seeming distorted! This kind of illusion reveals the importance of the context in vision, as a background may influence the way we see objects.

THE MORE SQUARED SQUARE, page 53
99% of people say A, but it is actually B. You do not believe it? Check it with a set square. In cases of perceptive distortion, the brain interprets incorrectly. It rectifies wrongly regular lines or shapes in the foreground in contrast to other regular lines or shapes in the background by making them appear distorted.

LINE UP, page 54
Both pairs of lines are actually perfectly straight and parallel, but lines A seem more straight than lines B. Color is also important regarding the perception of illusions of distortion. When we reduce the light contrast (isoluminance) some optical effects tend to vanish.

MYSTERIOUS DRAWINGS, page 55

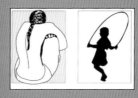

They represent a woman seen from behind and a girl playing. Puzzles that resemble abstract drawings you have to give a sense are known as droodles. These kinds of puzzle were popularized in the U.S. by Roger Price's 1953 book *Droodles*. The trademarked name 'droodle' is a portmanteau word suggesting both 'doodle' and 'riddle', but the droodles or indovinelli grafici have been known since the Renaissance in Italy. One of the oldest droodles – representing a blind beggar behind a street corner – was drawn by the Italian painter Agostino Carracci (1557–1602).

POSSIBLE OR NOT?, page 56

None as they are all what we call impossible objects, that is, objects that cannot exist according to the known laws of physics, but have a representation suggesting, at first sight, that they can be constructed.

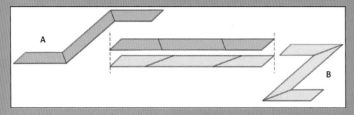

CARPETS, page 57

Both carpets are the same length (see above) so the work is even.

TANGRAMAGIC, page 58

Actually, the figures do not disappear; they are just redistributed differently. The more figures there are, the shorter they are! (see image, left).

ADDING UP, page 59

This picture has a particular property – it can be viewed upside down as well! If you invert the picture the dice score 10! You can perform this as a trick; copy the image and show it to one of your friends, asking him to write on a sheet of paper the dice score, then invert the image and show it to another friend, repeating your request.

TWIN MAZES, page 60

See the images above and right.

MENTAL ARITHMETIC, page 61

33! Did you really count the dots or did you just deduce that equidistant points arranged in a regular cross are odd in number when there is one central dot?

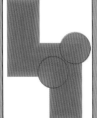

DIAGONALS, page 62

As shown in the image, there are no diagonals, just layers of colors (see left). This illusion is a striking perceptual effect related to lateral inhibition. The effect occurs when concentric geometrical figures of decreasing size and luminance are stacked one on top of another.

PASTA STILL LIFE, page 63

The color of the plate is brown (C) and the decorative circular line is reddish (2). The simultaneous color contrast makes the colors look very different!

TORQUATO PUZZLE, page 64

This game may have been given to Leonardo Pisano (the famous Fibonacci), by Chandlahuri, his Indian servant. Leonardo renamed this puzzle *lo joco enimmatico del brachiale torquato* (the puzzle of the twisted bracelet). The Torquato puzzle was inspired by the Chinese rings puzzle. To separate the string from the bracelet, follow the steps shown in figs. a) to i). When you arrive at step i), repeat the operation depicted in figs. f), g) and h) once again. To replace the string in the puzzle again, see the starting disposition in the image on the left. The Torquato puzzle is a topological puzzle. Poetically speaking, topology is a fascinating area of mathematics where you bend your mind around the curves of reality. More prosaically, topology is the study of geometric properties that are preserved under deformation. Sometimes topology is referred to as "rubber sheet geometry" because it does not distinguish between a circle and a square (a circle made out of a rubber band can be stretched into a square), but does distinguish between a circle and a figure eight (you cannot stretch a figure eight into a circle without tearing). Torquato is made of a closed loop (the braid) interlaced with an open loop (the string). It has at one end a locking loop (the cardboard piece with the hole) and at the other end an end loop (the other cardboard piece). Since we can free the string from the braid bracelet we can consider the closed and open loops as two unlinked rings.

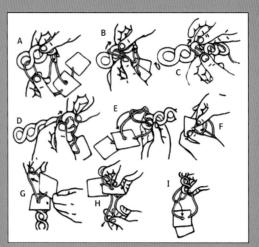

COLOR YIN YANG, page 65

Not at all! The semicircular shape in the pink yang symbol is actually grey and not green, and the color of the semicircular shape in the green yin is darker than the opposite pink yang symbol.

DISTORTED LEGS, page 66

Straight! Take a pencil or a ruler and check it. This is a variant of the Fraser illusion.

DISTORTED SQUARE, page 67

No, it is a square with perfect right angles! The illusion is induced by the alternating clear and dark dots and may be related to the Café Wall Illusion.

UNDISRUPTED SKETCH, page 68

Such a drawing is called a unicursal curve – one that you get when you put your pencil down and draw until you get back to the starting point. As you draw, your mark can intersect itself, but are not supposed to have any triple intersections. Unicursal or continuous curves or network puzzles, have been known since ancient times. One of the earliest is the *lunulae* of Allah which consists of two intersecting *lunulae*.

THE WISE PIRATE, page 69

Blackbeard received 66 gold pieces (396 / 6 = 66), because his proposal was "I would share the booty with only five selected pirates, so that each one of us will receive 66 gold pieces instead of 36. I know this isn't fair, but the Iron Pirates' Law allows me to do it!" Before voting he took the five greediest pirates aside and described to them what they stood to gain in voting for him…

CHECKERED ROWS, page 70

Believe it or not, the bricks in the picture are arranged in exactly parallel rows, even if the rows within the center of the picture seem to diverge. This illusion is known as the Cafe Wall Illusion. Dr. Richard Gregory and Priscilla Heard first described it in 1979. Orientation-sensitive simple cells in the brain's striate cortex cause the apparent tilt of the mortar gray lines. Our brain interprets two unaligned bricks of the same color lying one on top of the other, as a diagonal band that interferes with the gray mortar line between the blocks making it tilt in the direction of the diagonal band.

SQUARING FISH, page 71

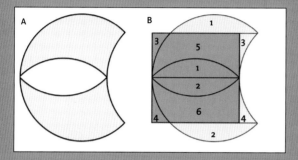

First, assemble the body of the fishes as shown in fig. a. Then cut out the shapes in to six pieces as depicted in fig. b.

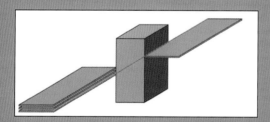

MISALIGNED EDGES, page 72

The edge of the lower shelf on the left is a continuation of the edge of the single shelf. This illusion is a variant of the Poggendorff illusion, one of the most popular distortion illusions. Although much has been written about it since its discovery in 1860, the underlying mechanism that produces this effect is still not well understood. Some theories suggest that we have orientation detectors that exaggerate all acute angles and minimize all obtuse angles. So, when a diagonal crosses a perpendicular bar, we give a different angular value to each visible segment of the diagonal.

THE STRANGEST HORSE RACE, page 73

Some people may think the old man told them that the prize for winning the race with the slowest horse was to get to clean out the horse stalls! However, there is another logical reason. According to the old man's suggestion, they swapped over and rode each other's horses! In this way, they transformed an infinite race into a competitive race. Anyone riding the horse of his competitor tries to make it win for a simple reason; the rule of the race states that whoever has the slowest horse wins.

COLOR ALIGNMENT, page 74

No, as only diagonals of the same color can be linked together by a continuous diagonal line (see left). This illusion is related to the Poggendorff illusion.

CONCENTRIC?, page 75

The rings are perfectly concentric and the impression of motion is mainly due to the bad integration of motion signals in our brain.

MATHEMATICAL GAME OF GOOSE, page 76

If you are lucky the minimal number of tosses is six. You would actually have to get a six on five consecutive throws followed by a two (or get a six four times and a four twice). You cannot reach disc 16 with the very first throws, because 16 is not divisible by three (remember you have to triple the numbers of your die). Thus, you have to cover the route of the board game twice in order to have a chance to reach your goal (in fact, two times 40 plus 16 equals 96 which is divisible by three). Dividing 96 by the largest number of the die (6x3=18), we obtain 96:18=5 with six discs left to cover.

CRETAN MAZE, page 77

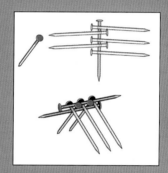

NAIL MATTER, page 78

Arrange the nails as shown (above right), and place the seventh nail across the top. Slowly pick up the entire bundle by the bottom nail. The heads of the interwoven nails should lock on to the top nail.

imagination test, page 79

Figure A represents an open chocolate box with a defect, while B is a ladder leant against a mirror. Completion figures and indovinelli grafici are based on the *pareidolia*—an innate human tendency to impose a pattern on random or ambiguous shapes.

INTERLOCKED DISK, page 80

Yes. The secret is to move all three pieces at the same time as shown in the illustration. Such puzzles belong to the family of the planar burrs, two-dimensional interlocking puzzles that require a certain number of moves to free the pieces.

GUESS THE IMAGES, page 81
Picture A represents an elephant standing on its forelegs while picture B shows a pair of cats drinking milk from a bowl.

CONNECTION DILEMMA, page 82

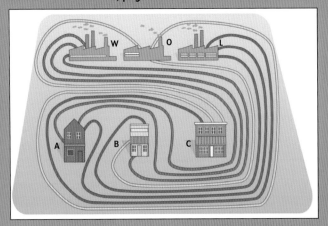

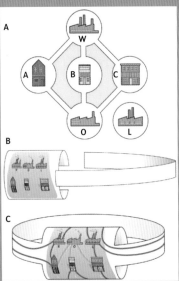

Each year we receive an extraordinary number of letters regarding a similar classic route problem. Once and for all we would like to state that it is not possible to connect the buildings W, O and L to each of the three houses without crossing a pipe. If we differentiate with colors the relative connections that start from the utility suppliers W, O and L, we can see on the diagram that houses A and C are connected twice to the same supplier. Why is it impossible to solve this puzzle in two dimensions? Have a look at the diagram above and you will understand that three connections starting from two utility suppliers will inevitably enclose one of the houses, preventing it from being connected to at least one utility supplier. However, this puzzle is possible to solve by using subterfuge! Reproduce the drawing on paper, then roll it up to form a cylinder and add a paper strip as shown in fig. b. The final image shows how the puzzle should appear and how the houses A, B and C are finally connected to the utility suppliers. Maths enthusiasts can use the Euler graph formula (V - E + F = 1) to discuss and prove that this puzzle is unsolvable.

TWO IN ONE, page 83
The bars seem to wobble. This illusion is induced by alignment of tilted squares. The foreground image consists of a grid of evenly-spaced squares where the squares are scaled to show darkness and rotated to show gradients in the image. When you move two metres away from the picture you will see a cat. This image was created by Craig S. Kaplan, an assistant professor of computer science at the University of Waterloo in Ontario, Canada.

UNDER THE ARCHES, page 84
The perspective of the arches creates a complete disconnection that is visually quite believable. However, the top and bottom parts of the arcade are at different angles. Adding to the effect is the fact that whilst the top part is linear, there are a series of angular structures at the bottom.

SLANTED STRUCTURE, page 85
No, the structure is perfectly straight up and down and all rows are perfectly horizontal. This illusion is related to the Frazer illusion.

HIDDEN 3D, page 86

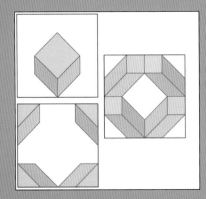

As you can see from the image (left), there are nine solid figures. The puzzle picture represents what is known as a multistable figure and means there are more than two ways to interpret it. Visual perception involves co-ordination between sensory sampling of the world and active interpretation of the sensory data. Human perception of objects is ordinarily stable and robust, but it falters when presented with patterns that are ambiguous or multistable. Patterns including ambiguous cubes that can be read as solid or hollow according to the way we imagine they are lit up are popular. They are often used to decorate objects such as the backs of playing cards.

COAXIAL RINGS?, page 87
Yes, the circular bands of alternate red and black squares are perfectly concentric. Strangely, the illusion effect vanishes when the image is reduced or seen from a distance. This is a neat Fraser illusion variant.

KEEP YOUR DISTANCE, page 88
Both paths have the same length. This is a very old puzzle, but one we still love to modify and use.

ANTIQUE TAPESTRY, page 89
The rows are perfectly straight and parallel to each other. This illusion resembles both the Café Wall illusion and Fraser illusion.

BOWLED OVER, page 90
The first object seems more concave than the second one due to the way we interpret the reflection of the light on observed objects. Our brain has a convexity preference; it assumes that light comes from above and uses this assumption to infer the convexity. In reality, the image represents two copies of the exact object, rotated 180 degrees from each other.

PERPETUAL MOTION?, page 91
Obviously, since nine is greater than six, the side of the wheel with the nines is heavier; thus it should rotate in the direction shown by the arrows. This perpetual motion device works thanks to the rotational symmetry that transforms a '6' into a '9', and vice versa. The same principle works with Roman numerals such as IX and XI. The apparent motion of the wheel is mainly due to the color and light contrasts of the image. It occurs well in our peripheral vision. If you gaze steadily at the wheel it will be stationary.

EVERGREEN?, page 92
The background color is an even green. The thin dark and white outlines of the patterns create a Bezold effect, making some regions look darker or lighter than they really are. The Bezold effect is an optical illusion named after German professor of meteorology Wilhelm von Bezold (1837–1907). He discovered that a color might appear different depending on its relation to adjacent colors.
Baingio Pinna, an Italian researcher in the field of vision, used color outlines on a white background instead of black and white outlines on a color background and obtained quite different effects. He called these kinds of illusions watercolor illusions, according to him a phenomenon of long-range color assimilation. It occurs when a dark chromatic contour delineating a figure is flanked on the inside by a brighter chromatic contour, making it seem as if the brighter color spreads into the entire enclosed area.

PANDORA'S VASE, page 93
Dot C. Obviously the surface of the vase above dot C is considerably larger than the surface below it. This discrepancy tends to confuse our mind and make accurate distance estimation difficult.

LIGHT BALLS, page 94
Ball B. The color green tends to appear more yellowish within a dark blue environment which why most of us will have selected ball A instead of ball B!

TRANSFORMATIONS, page 95

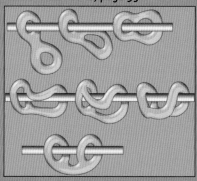

You can solve this puzzle using a topological method called continuous transformation as depicted (left). Topology deals with the ways that surfaces can be twisted, bent, pulled, or otherwise deformed from one shape to another without tearing or cutting.

COME CLEAN, page 96
No, the three red labels are all the same size. The perspective angles they are viewed at make them appear very different.

GEOMETRY, page 97
Curvilinear tessellations were very appreciated by Islamic artists for decorating palaces and mosques. Circular and curvilinear dissections are however less common than rectilinear dissections because of the 'unsquarable property' of the circle.

IMPERFECT TRIANGLE, page 98

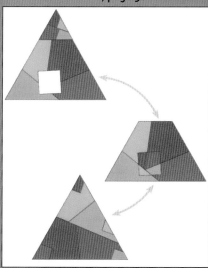

This geometric puzzle is based on Dudeney's triangle. Henry Ernest Dudeney (1857 – 1930) was an English author and mathematician who specialized in logic puzzles and mathematical games. He is known as one of England's foremost puzzle creators. His major work was *Amusements in Mathematics*. Some of Dudeney's most famous innovations were his 1903 success at solving the Haberdasher's puzzle – cutting an equilateral triangle into four pieces so it can be rearranged to make a square – and publishing the first known crossnumber puzzle in 1926.

SYMBOLIC, page 99
No; each pair of letters is exactly the same size. This illusion is based on the Ebbinghaus illusion.

AREAS, page 100
The shapes with the same area are the blue square, the yellow and the orange triangles. The shapes with the same perimeter are the yellow and orange triangles and the concave green shape. The shapes with the same surface are the yellow and orange triangles. The shapes at the bottom of the page all have the same area.

MATCHMAKER, page 101
Follow the instructions to solve the problem:

IMPOSSIBLE TRIANGLE?, page 102

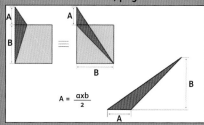

$$A = \frac{a \times b}{2}$$

You just need the most basic knowledge of mathematics to solve this puzzle. The area of the triangle is simply two times five divided by two, equalling five square inches. The visual proof confirms this.

TRIADS, page 103
The number is nine. The trick is based on the fact that adding three consecutive numbers of any arithmetical series you obtain a multiple of three and the sum of the digits of a multiple of three is also a multiple of three.

THE WARRIOR AND THE TORII, page 104

The warrior is a bistable image and the second warrior lies in the upper part of the image (a). The torii is actually an impossible figure made of two elements seen from different points of view (b).

LIGHT BULB ILLUSION, page 105
No, the yellow background color is uniform. A change in apparent brightness happens if you move closer and further away from the image.

THE MAGIC DOLLAR, page 106
A lot of people do not understand where the trick is. That it is an example of how badly formulated problems can lead to confusion and false conclusions. You only have to consider two things: firstly, that the money the service supplier (manager and blameworthy clerk) effectively received was $195 - $25 + $13 = $183. Secondly, the money the three students effectively paid was $195 - $12 = $183; Then you can see that A = B.

STRAIGHT OR NOT?, page 107
Neither. The lines are straight and parallel – another version of the Zöllner illusion.

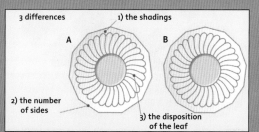

OBSERVATION TEST, 108
See image, left.

THE TEMPLE OF HORUS, page 110

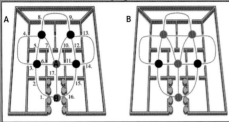

It is only possible to solve the puzzle when not more than two rooms have odd numbers of doors (representing the departure and the arrival points, see A). Therefore the Horus Temple Puzzle is solvable. However, when door C is open the conditions change and you have three rooms with an odd number of doors, (b). This renders the puzzle unsolvable. Swiss mathematician Leonhard Euler discovered the theory behind this puzzle. He developed the graph theory to solve the famous Königsberg bridge problem. There were seven bridges over the River Pregel at Königsberg in Prussia and Euler proved conclusively that there was no way of traversing each bridge once and only once, starting and returning at the same point in the town.

WIRED, page 111

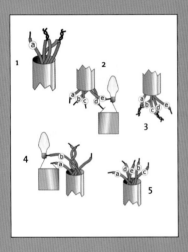

First, label any wire A and connect the other wires together into two pairs (1). Then go down to the ground floor. Begin testing wires with the light bulb and the battery to see which can pair into a circuit (2). One wire will not complete a circuit; this is wire A. Label B, C, D and E the two pairs of wires which complete the circuit and then connect together the wires as shown and return to the second floor (3).

Untie the ends of the pairs of previously connected wires, but keep them grouped by twisting as shown. Start testing (4). The wire that completes the circuit with A is B; the wire twisted with B is C; the wire that completes the circuit with C is D. One wire will not complete a circuit – E (fig. 5).

SIZE DISTORTION, page 112

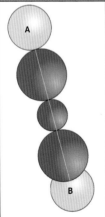

Most readers will answer 'Yes', but the actual answer is no. The alignment of purple balls will shift ball B because it is larger than the distance that separates balls A and B (see the solution image). This is an interactive adaptation of the Müller-Lyer illusion.

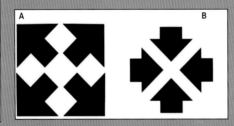

TO THE POINT, page 113

There are 48 arrows! There are two sets of arrows that are not easy to perceive (see A and B). This is a figure-ground perceptual illusion based on the fact that we tend to perceive a figure that stands out from the background.

ENCHANTED STAIRCASE, page 115

Starting from A and going to the left to cross the bridge the jogger woman will climb and go down 14 steps. Starting from A and going to the right, instead, she will climb and go down only 10 steps. This is a tricky optical illusion based on the Penrose staircase – a two-dimensional depiction of a staircase in which the stairs make four 90-degree turns as they ascend or descend yet form a continuous loop, so that a person could climb them for ever and never get any higher.

MAGIC MIRRORS, page 116

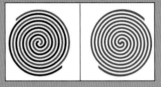

Katoptrons A and B both contain a decorative spiral design. However, the design in katoptron A represents two different spirals, while the design in katoptron B represents just one double spiral. These figures were adapted from a visual test made by psychologists Marvin L. Minsky and Seymour A. Papert.

A QUESTION OF GEOMETRY, page 117

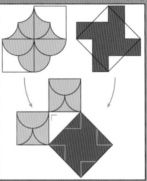

The curvilinear shape A can be dissected into two squares and the cross-shaped figure B into a larger square. Thanks to the Pythagorean theorem we can demonstrate that they are of the same area (as depicted below). During this operation no pieces are superimposed nor placed side by side. For those who have forgotten it, the Pythagorean theorem states that in any right triangle the area of the square whose side is the hypotenuse (the side of a right triangle opposite the right angle) is equal to the sum of areas of the squares whose sides are the two legs (i.e. the two sides other than the hypotenuse).

MAGIC STARS, page 118

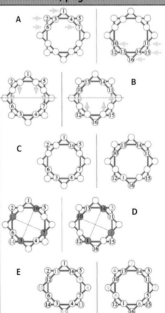

a) Fill in numbers 1 to 7 top down, left to right or numbers 16 to 10 bottom up, right to left b) Shift numbers 6, 3 and 4, 7 (or numbers 10, 13 and 14, 11) to the mirror nodes in accordance with the symmetric line. c) Place number 16 next to 1 or 1 next to 16 as shown. d) Consider now the numbers in the blue discs. The sum of two opposite numbers should be equal to the sum of the other pair of opposite numbers. e) Finally, filling out the rest of the numbers is easy since each line should add up to 34. Fill first the lines containing three numbers (blue numbers), then progressively with the green and orange numbers.

WATER DROP EFFECT, page 119

Yes; the lines within the water drops are perfectly colinear and also perpendicular to the page. This is a simultaneous orientation contrast effect. Since the lines are surrounded by lines tilting slightly to the right, our brain tends by compensation to lean the vertical lines in the opposite direction.

KNOT PROBLEM, page 120

Both! Take a piece of string, reproduce the arrangement and try for yourself.

RED PEPPER YELLOW PEPPER, page 121

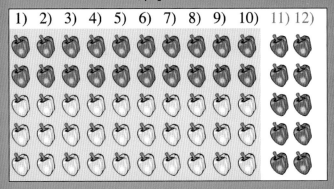

As you can see from the image, the red and yellow sweet peppers make ten groups of five sweet peppers you can reasonably sell for two euros. The last two groups are made only with red sweet peppers that cost effectively much more than two euro, the price at which they have been sold! Therefore the loss of one euro depends on the price difference of these last ten red sweet peppers.

THE FOOTPRINT ILLUSION, page 122

Did you notice that the footprints appear embossed as though they are rising up above the beach? This is an optical illusion caused by our brain's convexity preference. When this photograph was made, the camera was pointing straight down at the ground. However, we changed the orientation of the photo. You look at pictures supposing that sunlight comes from above, so shadows should appear on the bottom of objects. By flipping the photo 180 degrees, the footprints will look correct (see picture above). Right?

MAGIC MAGIC SQUARE, page 124

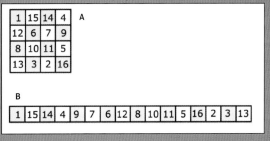

The total is always 34! The numbers contained in the magic square have the strange property that the sum of all the numbers in the yellow cells (68) is equal to the sum of the numbers in the white cells (see fig. a). During the experiment, when you fold the cells, you actually fold alternating yellow and white cells (fig. b) folding unconsciously each yellow cell back over each white cell. Thus, any way you fold and cut the magic square the total stays still the same. You can now perform this trick on your friends!

LEANING TOWER PAINTINGS, page 125

The last painting on your right.

THE RED SPOT, page 127

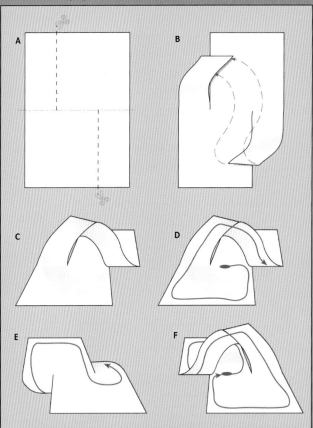

Cut the paper along the marked lines according to fig. a in the illustration and paste the two strips of paper together as shown in fig. b and c. Make a spot on the middle of the page and trace a continuous line which covers both the front and the back of the paper sheet (see fig. d, e and f). Your path is approximately twice the perimeter of the page.

ANTIQUE MAGIC SQUARE, page 128

First fill the cells of the square with numbers as shown in the first picture. Then interchange the numbers at both ends of the arrowed diagonals.

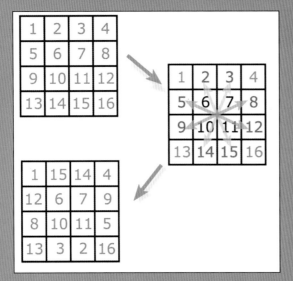

MORE GUESS THE IMAGE, page 129

Picture A represents a Chinese banquet before the arrival of the guests while picture B shows three ghosts looking down a well.

TO SHAVE OR NOT TO SHAVE?, page 130

If you use classical logic this paradox is unsolvable because if the barber does not shave himself, he must abide by the rule and shave himself and if he does shave himself, according to the rule he will not shave himself.

However, using your wit you can find that the barber belongs neither to the group of men who shave themselves, nor to those whom he does shave, because the barber is a woman! Another possible solution is that the barber belongs to both groups because he has a perfect clone we will call Barber #2. So Barber #2 shaves only himself and Barber #1, who alternately shaves only those men who do not shave themselves (excluding himself and Barber #2). The barber paradox is often attributed to the mathematician Bertrand Russell.

TRIANGULAR DIFFERENCES, page 131

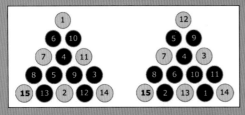

There is more than one solution. Try to find another original solution as opposed to those we have illustrated!

DIVERGING SLATS, page 132

Yes; they are perfectly straight and parallel although they seem to diverge. This is another variation of the Café Wall illusion.

MIND CONTROL, page 133

This is a real mission impossible because if someone tells you not to think of a red fish, you are not going to be able to think of anything else but a red fish! This shows that the full control of the mind is an illusion.

THE GREAT ELEPHANT DILEMMA, page 134

Whatever the elephant does, it will be the wrong thing. If it releases the mouse, the mouse has guessed incorrectly, so it should be squashed. However, if the elephant does squash the mouse, it is bound to release it because the mouse has guessed correctly. This dilemma is based on an apparently unsolvable problem in logic dating back to ancient Greece.

OBSERVATION TEST, page 135

The succession of alternating yellow and blue crosses produces a visual distortion. If the crosses were all the same color, there wouldn't be any illusion. This demonstrates that small changes can be very significant in the field of visual perception.

TRIANGULAR KANGAROO, page 136

See the solution image below.

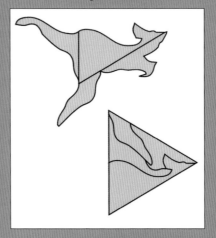

THE ILLUSIVE LABYRINTH, page 137

You cannot complete the labyrinth because it is a closed form. Such peculiar shapes are called Jordan's curves.

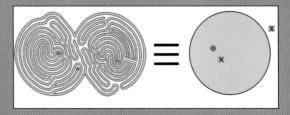

FOUR-PIECE PUZZLE, page 138

The player who has puzzle A will win the challenge! By switching the pieces A-D and C-B, it is easy to obtain a square without a hole, unlike puzzle B whose pieces are kites having adjacent sides equal in pairs so that if you switch these pieces (k-n, l-m) you obtain the same square again and again.

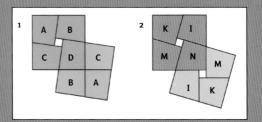

ARCHAEOLOGICAL MAZE, page 139

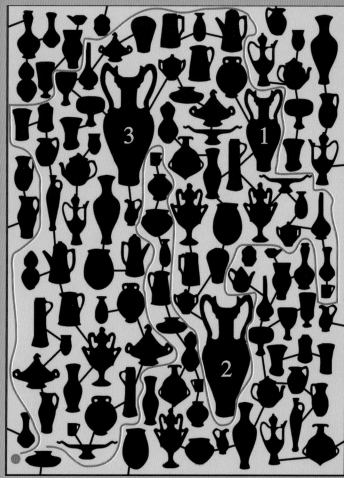

THE THREE-TAILED DOG, page 140

Even if the philosopher Lao-Tsu says "Recognize the utility of what does not exist!", in real life you cannot take into consideration and add what does not exist (no dog). This problem is similar to the classic 'half-full glass equals a half-empty glass'; if you multiply both terms by two, you obtain one full glass equalling one empty glass. That is clearly nonsense!

AN OPEN AND SHUT CASE, page 141

Wire puzzle B.

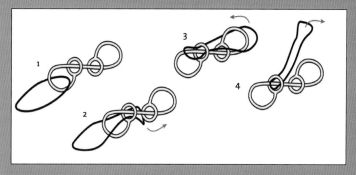

A QUESTION OF DISTANCE, page 142

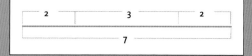

The answer is zero square miles. The length of three sides of the plot is equal to the length of its largest side. This makes the plot a line! See the solution illustration to confirm this.

ANOTHER QUESTION OF AREA, page 143

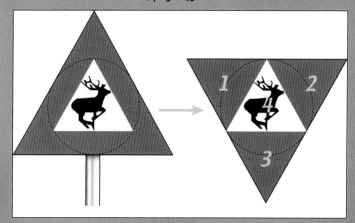

The illustration visually demonstrates that the white equilateral triangle is one fourth of the total area of the warning sign. Therefore its area is 100 divided by four, equaling 25 square inches.

AREA AGAIN, page 144

The image visually demonstrates that the red diagonal is also the radius of the dial, thus the distance that separates the hands of the turnip watch is four divided by two equalling two inches.

ENOUGH INFORMATION?, page 145

You can see in the image that the quadrilateral shape can be dissected into a right triangle which is half a square having each side 40 ins long. Therefore its area is 40 multiplied by 40 divided by two equalling 800 square inches.

STAR TRANSFORMATION, page 146

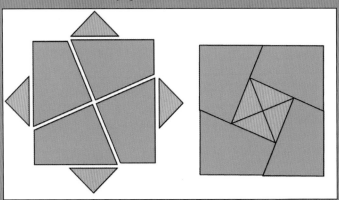

ANOTHER OBSERVATION TEST, page 147

Most of the readers say two or three different patterns, but there is only one kind of blue pattern. The blue patterns look different because the regularity of their shape is perturbed by the background.

I HAD A DREAM, page 148

The doors that remain open at the end are those that have been opened/closed an odd number of times. Only the doors which have a perfect square number are opened/closed an odd number of times, because in the other numbers the factors always go in twos: for example 45 equals 1x45, 3x15, 5x9 (six factors), whereas the square number 36 equals 1x36, 2x18, 3x12, 4x9 and 6x6 (nine factors). The base number six counts only once. The doors that remain open at the end are therefore the doors having square numbers: 1, 4, 9, 16, 25, 36, 49, 64 and 81. The winning numbers have two digits and they are 16, 25, 36, 49, 64 and 81.